LE HALLE BLANC

---

from: P.M.

to: Cabinet

Liberty,
Equality and
Fraternity

All debate on the above
will be subject to the
guillotine.

Are WE'RE THE FRENCH REVOLTING?

THE COMPLETE GUIDE TO THE
FRENCH REVOLUTION 1789–1989

David Fine

Cartoons by
Ian Kellas

ALAN SUTTON
1989

ALAN SUTTON PUBLISHING
BRUNSWICK ROAD · GLOUCESTER · UK

ALAN SUTTON PUBLISHING INC
WOLFEBORO · NEW HAMPSHIRE · USA

First published 1989

British Library Cataloguing in Publication Data

Fine, David
Were (are) the French revolting? : or the complete guide to the French Revolution, 1789–1989.
I. Title.
828'.91407

ISBN 0-86299-693-7

Library of Congress Cataloging in Publication Data
applied for

Designed by Richard Bryant and Martin Latham
Cover Design by Martin Latham
Cover Illustration by Ian Kellas
Typesetting and origination by
Alan Sutton Publishing Limited.
Printed in Great Britain by
Guernsey Press Co. Limited, Guernsey,
Channel Islands.

CONTENTS

To
Richard

THE CREDITS AT THE END OF THE UNIVERSE

by Alpha-Soixante

IT NEVER HAPPENED. Everybody thought it did, and made a great fuss about it, almost as much fuss as the dope-testing scandal in the Wellington Boot Hurling Contest of the XXIII Steroid Games, but the French Revolution never actually happened. That is the funniest thing about it.

Alpha-Soixante looked up the Manual. 'Revolutions: – See Circles.' Under Circles it said: 'See Revolutions.' The Manual was a vast improvement upon The Book. It contained everything The Book had between its covers, but neatly arranged according to a logical order. This is why the French Revolution never happened.

Alpha-S scratched his head. Things were different now. They'd not been the same since taking voluntary redundancy from a film no one had ever heard of. After six months of twiddling his video-heads, he'd attended a Robot Retraining Course. It was either that or losing his benefit to sub-titles.

'The Book is out of date, a thing of the past,' the editorial board told him, 'it lacks historical depth.'

'Historical depth?' Alpha had exclaimed.

'That's right, Soixante. Historical depth.'

'But it contains the past, the present and future, under constant revision. In fact, everything.'

The editorial board gave him a bored look. One of tremendous and impersonal ennui. They had heard it all before. Nothing is new in this world.

'True,' they agreed. 'But it does not contain nothing. Absolutely nothing. Permit us to explain. History is only what people think happened, might have happened or wanted to have happened. However it cannot have happened since otherwise people wouldn't go to the trouble of thinking it did.'

'History is the greatest creation of all intelligent life forms,' a marketing executive added. 'It is what separates us from reality – and our competitors.'

'I see,' said Alpha-Soixante, rather wishing he hadn't. 'You want me to go into the field and find out what didn't happen.'

'Exactly.'

He found himself in a field. He took out The Manual to find his bearings. In its index, under 'History' it said:-

'See:–

An old part of him wanted to look up:-

To see if it said 'History.'

But he couldn't. Definitely an improvement. Less work to do.

The grass in the field was very green, soft, lush and inviting. Alpha-Soixante was tired after his long journey and he lay down. After a while a thick long sticky sand-papery thing rubbed the sprockets between his film-spools and focus-puller. He woke up to find a huge fat four legged creature with black splodges all over its white skin and a bell around its neck eating the grass methodically around his head. Two enormous bovine eyes stared back at him before returning to the grass. There were lots of them, all doing the same thing.

Alpha-S wondered whether or not he ought to as well. He didn't want to arouse the suspicions of the natives. They could turn nasty.

'They're cows.'

'What?'

'No. Cows. I've never seen a what.'

The voice came from the next field. There were no cows there. Nor, for that matter, whats. Instead there

was just earth, waiting for things to grow. That was why there were no cows there, The Manual told Soixante, when he looked up 'Ecology.'

'Are you a crop rotation, by any chance?'

'No,' replied the figure in the middle of the field, each arm stuck out of an old coat with a smiling face under an old hat.

'Then you must be a farmer.'

'No,' the figure said, still smiling. 'Wrong again.'

'An EEC subsidy?'

'What do you take me for!'

The smile began to get to Alpha-Soixante. It reminded him of a speaking door he'd once tried talking to, deep in the inky blackness of the entertainments industry. There was no escape.

'So what are you doing here?'

'I thought you'd never ask,' the scarecrow replied. 'Waiting for a Swede to invent dynamite so I can win the Nobel Prize for being out standing in my own field.'

'Ah, I see,' remarked Soixante, feeling as though he was back in front of the editorial board again. 'And those are – cows.'

'I've just said so, haven't I? There's Louis XVI and Talleyrand, next to them's Danton, in the corner's Marie-Antoinette and Robespierre. Mirabeau and Mirabeau are at the bottom, near the gate. Can't see Bonaparte, must be somewhere there though.'

Alpha recorded all their names at once. He had a terrible memory for names, and he might be able to use some of these for subtitles.

'So what do, er, Robespierre and –'

'Oh look, there's Marat.'

'And Marat do?'

'Eat grass. Not much else to do really. They've not invented the motor-mower yet. You don't eat grass now?'

'No.' Alpha-Soixante paused. 'I'm, I am an historian.'

'Like me, then. A man of leisure. I used to scare away birds but these mad Frenchies have shot them all.'

An idea floated through Alpha's rewind counter. The editorial board wouldn't go a bundle on a planet where just about everybody loafed around in fields eating grass all day, even if it was mostly harmless. Keep their names, get rid of their extra legs, turn their black blotches into stripey jumpers and he might be onto something.

His first efforts were admittedly dreadful, but after a while he got the hang of writing history. Plenty of action, plenty of thrills, but most of all lots of manic Frenchmen trying to change things.

He helped them along by inventing Paris. The rest is history.

Greizes and the Revolutionary Spirit

by P.G. Doghouse

IF YOU'VE EVER forgotten what you're meant to be doing while you're still doing it, then you'll know exactly what I'm talking about. Greizes appeared with le café au lait and croissant, fraîchement beurre, and the dashed thing slipped right out of my mind. I say Greizes, but what I mainly saw was his feet, since my head was under the bed at the time. We Roosters do not give of our best in such circs.

'You appear to have lost something, sir.'

'Yes, Greizes,' I replied, surfacing. 'The thread –'

'– Of your argument, sir?'

'Exactly.' The man's a marvel. Not lacking where it matters, and a Solomon amongst Philistines. It catches the Roosterish eye as it flicks to the racing pages.

A nom-de-plume, I believe, Greizes scribbles under in the modest vignettes he dashes off from time to time for the local rag au sujet philosophe. Solomon, that is, la jolly-old plume de ma tante, not the other coves, who wouldn't know a pearl of wisdom if a sackful smacked them in the face. Never one to mélange the facts as reported, the eminent Greizes. Quite the agent provocateur.

'Cardinal Rohan called, sir.'

The croissant, f.b., at once ceased to melt between the molars and turned to dust, rather akin to Lot's

wife, the one who became a pillar of salt. Said Cardinal
Rohan has the same effect upon yrs. trly. He is, to use
a phrase of Greizes, my Achilles something or other.
Suits of armour with the lid clamped down are no
proof. Mere mention of the name welds the Bertram
jaw in the goldfish position; one glance from the
excrescence's peepers frees the jaw but reduces the rest
to jellyfish with Saint Vitus Dance. Heel, that was the
word I was looking for. The man, amongst his other
redeeming features, is a heel of the first order. A
basilisk, as Greizes had once described him, in a
basilisk's clothing.

'I would not have thought to mention it, sir, but
the gentleman impressed upon myself the urgency of
his call.'

I gulped. Greizes proffered the Remy Martin and I
gulped again. The Rohan brood were still a bad
dream.

It had all been to do with the daughter, Ronette, a simpish little flit who spouted verse so wet she sounded like one of those thingamajigies they have at Versailles – fountains – without a plug-hole. The stuff floods everywhere. To my way of thinking, an early production model in the Creator's good scheme of things: lovely to look at, very latest lines in chic-ery, but not what the bruise between the ears would choose as a partner to share the hours in between dipping the c., f.b. into the c. au l. and knocking back the final R. Martin avant s'endormis. Marital fixtures such as these are to be avoided at all c-s.

But Ronette took my stupified silence as a strong man's way of saying oui, and the next thing I knew she'd wheeled me in before the eyes that burn holes through other basilisks, con brio, as a prospective son-in-law to incinerate. Greizes, as ever, came up with the goods. Fortified by quantities of fresh sea-bass, his immense brain rescued his master from a life-time chained to epic quatrains. Indicating my impromptu impersonation of a Portugese Man O'War with digitalis, he thought it best to inform old evil-eye that the affliction was alas, permanent, incurable and hereditary. All I had to do was jabber. I jabbered.

'Cardinal Death-Ray didn't say what he wanted?'

'Not in so many words, sir. The Monseigneur was inexact upon the point, though it seemed a matter of some agitation. He left believing you were not at home.'

'Good man, Greizes. Raise the stoney-faced draw-bridge, what.'

'I thought it wisest to bend before the storm, sir, as it were. The gentleman is not the most clement or affable I have had the fortune to meet. If I may make a personal remark, he leaves me –'

'Sweating at the gills?'

'A trifle ill at ease. Like the stripes, sir.' His

eyebrow raised a cat's whisker. This was serious stuff; brimstone-breathing back-to-front collars come and go, but stripes are stripes.

'Cardinal Rohan may, of course, sir, return.'

The goldfish impression popped up to do an encore.

'Send for the two-seater, Greizes, we leave for Chateau Pieralle at once. Do not spare the horses.'

'That would not be prudent, sir. Your Aunt Agathe is unable to receive guests. Les paysans have been somewhat troublesome of late. "Revolting," was the phrase which arose during conversation with her Ladyship's servants, sir. Your aunt, I would venture to suggest, is of a similar opinion.'

A woman of traditional views and strong feelings, the aged relative tends to use these mots justes to stymie her young nephew's sense of sartorial esprit de vivre. In her eyes the striped frock-coat was a blot on the boulevard, and it is her firm belief that I should leave such vital matters to my man, Greizes, as I do with everything else.

Up to a point I agree. Savant though the man is, in my estimation grey stuff between the ears too readily leads to slavish obedience of the conventional – the brain does not want to bother with buttons and bows, it wants to think. So be it.

Yet a chap must be free to express himself in the way he wishes – be it as a jelly-fish in stripes – or he is not a chap. The Rooster stripe is no idle whimsy but the vanguard of change and revolution to the stuffed chemises who clog gents outfitters. If Greizes has a fault, it is that his predeliction en appareil is just too grey and reluctant. If it wasn't for radicals like myself, we'd still be swanning around in the birthday s. like Adam and Eve, and then where would we be?

What this has to do with peasantry I don't know, so it came as a great surprise to the Rooster world-view to realise that Aunt Agathe bore an inkling of what a peasant was, still less whether or not they were in season. She leaves these chores to her game-keepers, being a salon-fillette at heart, preferring to stick to flower-arranging when she can't wangle out of feudal obligations for a swift beezer en ville chez moi. She can gavotte the hind legs off a flunkey, so surly oicks should have been nipped in the bud like a fleur-de-lys with an extra lys, or is it fleur? Even I could see that the general position re. rustic affairs was hardly buttercups and daisies.

'Not tugging their forelocks, Greizes, or bowing till the nostrils touch terra firma?'

'Amongst other things, sir. It may have escaped your notice, but Lady Pieralle appeared particularly upset over the circumstances of the Emperor.'

'That butcher's shop on four legs; it's Teddy's department. She doesn't give two hoots on a fiddle so long as her other half's in clover.'

Greizes paused in laying out the morning breeches.

'Unfortunately, sir, Lord Eduard is in a state far from bliss. If you recall, next week was to be the Auvergne and Puy de Nome massive boar contest, which the Emperor was considered by the cognoscente porcine as possessing a favourable chance in the super-heavyweight category.'

The feats of the Emperor are legion; cabinets stuffed to the gunnels with silverware in the Pieralle household bear testimony to the famed porker's abilities to clean up les fêtes agricoles. If anything is certain in life, then you could bet your chemise on this bulwark of boar trouncing the field without so much as an oink. Invincible, as Greizes once put it. He has a way with words.

'You mean Ted's pomme de s'oeil is off his trough, nobbled, and kidnapped?'

'Worse, sir. The peasants have eaten him.'

The Rooster constitution is best in adversity.

Though the gen. posish. with corrosive cardinals, sonneteering sirens, truculent thegns and polished-off pigs was indeed très serieux, it is at times such as these that young Bertram shows what he is made of.

'Tell dear Ted and Agathe that the Rooster household is theirs.'

'I took the liberty, sir, of already informing the Lord and Ladyship. She is arriving by the 5.47 from Clermont-Ferrand. Upon my advice, her husband has decided to travel abroad, to England, a village named Market Blandings which is well known amongst pig-breeders, I am told, for its Shropshire hogbacks.'

'To grieve the mortal loss and kindle the spirits anew, Greizes.'

'Something of that nature, sir. Shall I prepare the guest room?'

'And tell Monseignor Cataclysm, if he calls again, that I am at La Girondin.'

'But you are not a member, sir.'

'Well spotted, Greizes. I intend practicing my billiard shots at Les Parasites.'

'Very good, sir. I rather feel the reverend gentleman in question will be en route for some time. Realising the impending arrival of Lady Pieralle, I also took the liberty of informing him that you were intending to journey there later today, by the afternoon phanteon de grande vitesse.'

Miraculous. The man's a mindreader. Diet is what counts with thoroughbreds, Teddy and I are agreed upon that. Keeps the intellect keen. With Greizes in mid-season form and tucking into the Cod Mornay, double-portions, you would have seen Bertie Rooster about to trip along the boulevard as if he owned the place.

'The coat, sir.'

There was that edge to his voice, the hesitancy like a wine-taster used to a better class of plonk.

'Keep abreast of the times, Greizes. Chacun son goût. Laissez-faire. Your Voltaire fellow,' I continued, hoisting him by his own whojimiflip, '"What you wear gives me the heebie-jeebies, but I'll put the noggin on the block for your brass to wear it."'

'The gentlemen in question was referring to free-speech, sir. Dress is a different matter. As Georges-Louis Buffon states, "Style is the man himself."'

'And in my case, it's stripes.'

'Precisely, sir.'

Slipping on the alligator high-boots, I legged it for the South Quarter. There is no arguing with the man.

I cannot say I returned to the Rooster residence refreshed. Normally Les Parasites is a place where a chap can find innocent amusement away from the vicissitudes of life with a game of Blind-Man's Buff attempting to trip the valet with the odd billiard cue, or stuffing bread-rolls down the servant girls' chemiseries. Today these by-plays did not entertain. Duffy, Ouffy, Pouffy and Stuffy were out of sorts, malaised, if that's the word, and downright grumpy.

Even the famed Rooster stripe failed to lift. Something about Third Estate pipping L'Ancien Régime at the post, and at odds longer than Les Parasites' faces. I give these events short shrift, they're best left to Greizes's Solomon and his cronies, as I keep telling fellow members. Voltaire's guide to the turf is specific:- 'Once people begin to reason, all is lost.'

Or is it 'the people'? Must remember to ask Greizes. I may not understand friend Voltaire but I do know my place. Politics is definitely not the Rooster c. au l., too much having to kiss babies who require their mothers' attentions at the other end. Why anyone should devote their lives to these matters is one of the eighteenth-century's great unsolved mysteries. I have tried reading books on the subject, but they are like Ronette Rohan's verse, only flatter.

Greizes, of course, devours them by the boat-load, straight off the fish-monger's slab. A mind like his champs at the bit if not pondering this or that, and I'm sure it helps to keep his intellectual muscle lean and his encyclopaedic coat in lustrous fettle. The fish need something to work on.

After the second bracing R. M., he shimmered in to announce the arrival of Her Ladyship.

'Bon soir, Aunt Agathe,' I chimed.

'Bon soir, yourself, you blockhead. Where is it?'

'Where's what?'

'It.'

'It?'

'It. I am not getting through to you, numbskull. The necklace.'

'The necklace?'

'The necklace – O don't go into that saying-what-I've-just-said routine again, Bertie, or we'll be here till la fin du siècle. I said necklace and I mean necklace. Where is it?'

Aunt Agathe, though the worthiest relative any bachelor could have wished for, has a temper that makes Saul seem like Job on the back burner. Fired up, she's been known to sink ships at twenty leagues and stop the leaning tower of Pisa from leaning. I can see why Ted keeps to pigs. Whatever else these four-legged fellows do, they don't destroy all living life in sight when a spot of jewelry goes astray. Pigs don't wear jewelry, apart from a ring through the nose, as Greizes would be the first to confirm. Even wild boars with bunions are placid creatures compared to Aunt Agathe with her gander up. And her gander was up.

'Oh that necklace,' I tried airily. 'I thought you meant –'

'You haven't the faintest what I meant, cloth-brain.'

Greizes, as ever, came to rescue. Sang-froid perso-

nified, he manifested the string of pearls from about his person, and at once Aunt Agathe from being a harridan from hell resumed her usual sweetness and light.

'I found it whilst clearing up after you were gone, sir.'

'Under the bed?' I asked in a searing flash of deduction.

'No, sir. In your bookcase, between Aesop and Xenophon.'

'Smart thinking, the pair of you,' chipped in Aunt A. 'No one but Bertie would be dumb enough to think of putting it there and only Greizes would think of looking. The last time you stared at a book that wasn't about horses was before Gutenberg invented the printing press.'

I thought this stiff. Though I admit being partial to a flutter on the turf as much as the next man, how many of them can claim second prize in the Sunday School Bible Class for seven year olds and under?

'Whose jewels are they, Aunt. Yours?'

'Of course not. Do you think I'd trust you with something of mine, you chicken-brained dunderhead? I've seen sieves with better memories than yours. While you were down at Chateau Pierelle last month, I asked you to borrow – steal is too strong a word – the necklace from Cardinal Rohan in order to get you off the hook with her daughter.'

'What was he doing with a necklace in the first place?'

'It was a dowry present to the happy couple. Probably burgled from the Vatican.'

'Then why did I have to steal it? I'd have got the bally thing anyway and then bunged it on to you.'

'Only after the wedding, Bertie, dearest.'

'I see. The devil and the –'

'– Deep blue sea, sir? Your temporary lapse of

memory may have been due to a moderate over-indulgence before and after the event.'

Greizes, as usual, had hit the nail on the head. Judging by the state of mine the morning after, if there are different degrees of squiffiness, then the night in question had seen B. Rooster Esq. well and truly squiffed. I needed to be. Second Prize in the Under-Seven Old Testament Handicap may be a sound preparation for most things in life, but filching the dowry before the dowry is done is not one of them. Not when your protective pop-in-law drains blood merely by staring at his victims.

'So, Aunt A, what do you and Ted want with these cursed gems?'

She gave me one of those looks, which if they do not kill, have the obituary writers sharpening their quills. She is like Greizes; no arguing with either of them. That, as the poet said, seemed to be that, when a thunderbolt hammered between my ears and the grey areas seemed given over to producing that stuff that begins with E – Saint Elmo's fire.

'Is it permanent, Greizes, or merely seasonal?'

'The Cardinal asked a similar question, your Lady-ship. I believe the young master quivers like an aspen because the Cardinal called this morning and your nephew now has the impression that it was due to the disappearance of the pearls.'

'And it is?'

'No, your Ladyship, it is not.'

I stopped aspening, fished the demi-lunette from the Remy Martin, and stuck it back into business, Rooster once more ready to face the world.

'It was, I believe, your Ladyship, to do with his daughter, Ronette. He used a rather common expression whose precise meaning eludes me, but the gist of it was that Mr Rooster had been dipping his croissant in his daughter's café au lait and his daughter now has

a gâteau in the oven. The Monseignor was sore aggrieved.'

'You betcha,' laughed Aunt Agathe as the demi-lunette went walk-abouts. 'Can Cardinals have children? Been overindulging, young Bertie, while your aunt's elsewhere? He follows after his father, you know,' she continued, giving Greizes the conspiratorial wink, to which he cat-whiskered the e-brow.

Former members of Les Parasites have fond memories of Aunt A.'s youth. 'Agathe, the Amorous Agate,' they called her. Notwithstanding recent events, she has calmed down to find contentment in the sticks, with the odd fling centred on the Rooster pied-à-terre. A woman with a past and a hidden passion for pearls, of wisdom or otherwise.

The doorbell rang. Greizes was back before you realised he had gone. Cardinal Rohan was at the door, I fell to the floor.

'As I suspected, sir,' he remarked, helping me to my feet. 'Having found the situation at Chateau Pierelle not as he had anticipated, he has returned post-haste to ascertain why.'

'That's all very well, Greizes, but when he finds me here, he will not be eager to debate the whys and wherefores with myself, but either force me to marry the wretched Rohan rhymer woman or leave this earth in a lead-lined box. The devil of the devil and the deep blue sea.'

'Well put, sir. My prognosis entirely.'

Yes, but dash it all, what do we do?'

'Under the bed, Bertie,' ordered the aged r., eyes warming up to broiling temperature. 'I'll sort him out.'

Once more that day I had a mouse-level view of proceedings. Readers may be expecting a clash of titans. On the one hand Cardinal Spine-Chiller Rohan, on the other, Lady Agathe Greek-Fire Pierelle, both undefeated too. Forget the irresistable forces and

immovable objects bit, the reader wants to know the odds and where to put the family silver. I have to say the contest was singularly indecisive, a technical draw in the first round, if you can have such a thing. They looked at one another and both keeled over, out for the count, honours even.

I surfaced just in time to see Greizes finish administering the kiss of life to the aged aunt.

Il Cardinale was still out cold. The keenest polico would have never pecked away at the baby Rohan cheeks, had even his country's future depended upon it. Age did not improve the prospect. Nobly resisting the impulse to kick the jellyfish-maker where it hurts the most, I stepped across to congratulate Aunt A.

'Good shooting – a spot of night-life in celebration, old stick?'

'Cardinals bring out the best in me, I've been wanting to do that for ages. Can't stand these celestial worms who keep crawling in and out of the episcopal woodwork – No thank you, Bertie. Any other time, but I'm feeling a bit tired tonight. I think I shall go to bed and have an early evening. You toddle off and enjoy yourself, Greizes will tuck me in.'

'Righty ho, toodle-pip.'

I stopped at the door. Clouds still loomed on the Betram horizon.

'Sir?'

'Monseigneur Matchmaker.'

'Quite, sir. Perceiving the eventuality, I took the precaution of examining the Cardinal's cloak whilst he and her Ladyship were in conference, and finding a sealed document from the Archbishop, substituted one of my own devising. It states that the necklace is a gift to Her Highness Marie-Antoinette so that she may grant favour of the Court to the Cardinal's entreaties, but without the necklace the Monseigneur shall be – '

'Sunk.'

'Precisely, sir.'

'Greizes.'

'Sir?'

'Words fail me. What can I say?'

'Thank you, sir.'

Unbreeching the wallet, I proffered a healthy wedge of the clinking stuff. The man's a genius, worth more than the weight of the dearly departed and late lamented Emperor of L'Auvergne in solid gold Louis. It was the least I could do.

But it was no good. Considering which part of Gai Paris the Wooster stripe should make gaier, the spirit of selfless camaraderie came through on the rails.

'Take it,' I announced with leaden heart. 'And do with it what you will. Perhaps some of the poorer members of the evening debating society. Amongst the younger urchins, possibly?'

'The gesture will be appreciated, sir. If I may speak freely without embarrassment, there is likely to be a speech and a motion registering their regard of your self.'

'Just so long as it isn't too long and gums up proceedings. All these principles and proclamations, so much small print before the off. Beats me why anyone should want to read the stuff. Must rot their eyeballs.'

'"Happy," sir, "the people whose annuals are tiresome."'

'One of yours, Greizes?'

'Montesquieu. Will that be all, sir?'

Legion the occasion when I feel I ought to embrace the man, and this was one of them. But noblesse oblige, even in this day and age. Chipper than chipper, Rooster saw the loss of stripes in a broader light. Loss though it was to me, it was a gain to others. May they find as much fun in the red, white and blue.

Boldness More Boldness and Perpetual Boldness

Danton

Try Hairtonic

Robespierre

French Revolutionary Cooking

by Mandy Barriers

Chateau Turnover   serves masses

Ingredients
   One Royal Family
   A Seething Rabble
   5 Clubs of Debating Sugar
   3 Estates
   Principles to Taste
   Optional: One string of onions and a clove of garlic

Method
   Take the Royal Family, top and tail with a sharp
   guillotine and throw away the rest. If a guillotine is
   not at hand, a suitable sized axe will do in emergencies. Putting the family to one side, bring the
   Seething Rabble, preferably firm and juicy, to the
   boil and cook until the flesh begins to creep. Add
   the five Clubs of Debating Sugar – La Gironde,
   Jacobin and Cordeliers are generally considered the
   best – and stir well until the mixture is thick
   enough to stand alone. Make sure that any principles chosen do not clash or otherwise the mixture
   may stick to the melting pot or explode.

   While still hot, pour out to entirely cover Three
   Estates prepared earlier by constitutional methods.
   Wait until cool, then decorate with the tops of the
   Royal Family and serve.

LE 🦁🧄🧔 TE

CIVIC UNREST IN FRENCH

(from our own correspondent)

LE Soleil

FROGS GO HOPPING MAD!

NEWS SPECIAL

MPS

CAPITAL

L'express

PARIS IN TURMOIL
English Safe

THE STORMING OF THE BASTILLE

RBC2 Revolutionary Special

AND WE GO over to our match commentator, Bill the Scot, with expert summaries from former Triple Slam International, Bill the English.

Thank you, Desmond, and we welcome viewers to a glorious view of the approaches to the grand Bastille. Conditions are just about perfect for revolutionary activity, the going firm, with none of the morning's slipperiness that makes the cobbles such a difficult proposition. As you can see, there is a slight breeze blowing from right to left, rustling the banners of the proletariat, but not too strong since the flags atop the mighty fortress are virtually still. The combatants have enjoyed a spirited lunch together at the invitation of Governor Launay, while the windows and doors of the wee houses and shops in the alleyways nearby are just shuttered up. The capacity crowd is already in full voice awaiting the appearance of the two teams, treating us to their repertoire of patriotic songs in a hub-bub of anticipation. Each and every person here today, especially the droves of schoolboys perched in the trees along the terraces, is hoping for a fast, fluid game, whatever the outcome. So, the scene is set for an action-packed afternoon of revolutionary turmoil.

THE COMPLETE GUIDE TO THE FRENCH REVOLUTION

Well yes, Bill, it's always something to come to Paris, fantastic atmosphere and you never know what the French will throw at you – usually comes off in the bath, though.

I'm glad to hear it. And which of the two teams do you think will come off best today, William?

Difficult to say, Bill. The one thing you can always tell about the French is that they're unpredictable. The Imperial Forces, full of seasoned internationals, have a wealth of experience and composure to call upon whereas the Plebian Mob are rather more of an unknown quality up front. A lot may rest on whether or not they freeze on the big occasion and whether the Ancien Régime can last the distance, particularly in the final quarter when fitness levels count for so much.

And yet they've been having leadership problems of late.

Undoubtedly. It'll be interesting to see if the recall of Necker at Principal Minister will bring unity and cohesion to the Imperial play.

This is the third change they've made in less than five years. Brienne for Calonne, and then this last minute alteration with Necker back in for Brienne.

Yes, Brienne can consider himself unlucky perhaps; being the Queen's favourite, he might have expected a cardinal's hat rather than having to sit this one out. Presumably the selectors are hoping the experience and close game of Necker will help settle the situation, though he might find the pace a little lively after eight years out at the top level. No doubt the Republicans will be keen to pressure him with one or two high questioning kicks straight away.

And they do have a back division to exploit any weaknesses in their opponent's defence.

Quite right, Bill. Names like Talleyrand, Lafayette, Mirabeau, Sièyes, and Robespierre are all world-beaters. However I'm wondering whether the smaller

Republican forwards will secure enough decent first-phase possession from the set-pieces to allow their talents free reign across the revolutionary field.

So, with both sides having something to prove, trying to show that it's men against boys, no doubt it'll be a bruising physical encounter, but we have a real stromash in prospect.

Indeed, Bill. It is the French against the French, and as we've said, they are so unpredictable, anything could happen.

And the crowd's roar will tell you that the teams have just taken the field. The Ancien Régime, splendidly attired with plumed helmets and gleaming cuirasses defending the fortress end of this marvellous arena against the hordes of the Nouveau Republic. Hello, what's this? Now that's a real turn-up for the book. Necker, having been spectacularly recalled to international colours after eight years out in the wilderness, has himself been replaced at the pivotal position of Principal Minister by a relative unknown, Louis-Auguste Breteuil, from the Palace Club of Fontainebleau. And listen to the boos of the crowd, who don't like this one little bit.

Bad move by the Imperial Selectors, who've probably been unduly panicked by the recent rumours in the press and the streets of civil unrest. Although Jacques Necker might be a little short of pace these days, he is a fine player in defensive situations with just the level-headed expertise to settle his side. I know who I'd like to have behind me.

You don't think, William, that Breteuil being a favourite with the Queen might have anything to do with it?

Almost certainly. It now seems that the selectors are more concerned with saving their own skins than putting the best side out onto the park.

The other thing this sensational news means, of

course, is that it is highly doubtful the new Principal Minister will be able to play a direct role in the affairs of state until they're well underway. This very late call to colours leaves him stranded in Versailles at the moment, while the surging crowds welling towards this game have given the military no other option but to close the Sèvres and Saint-Cloud bridges. Perhaps Breteuil might be able to force his way through with the Montgolfiers brothers' hot-air balloon, but that is on duty here with the overhead cameras of the RDF.

His absence is sure to put a lot onto the shoulders of Governor Launay, who will need to step into the breach, otherwise the Imperials will be left rudderless in midfield. Yet he also has to try and conceal this weakness from the Parisian rabble. I wouldn't like to be in his boots today. Hell of a gamble to take.

So there's Bernard Jordan de Launay, who must've had quite a surprise over his croissants and coffee in his home on the Rue de Turenne, I can tell you, warming up under the battlements of the Bastille and encouraging his troops. What do you think is going through his mind, Bill?

Merdre.

Yes, he'll probably want to settle his side down and murder the opposition, figuratively speaking, that is. No easy task, I have to say that the Republicans, last year's wooden spoonists, are looking a highly confident outfit today. Without the style and glamour of their more well-known opponents, of course, don't be put off by their rather scruffy jerseys and ragamuffin sans-culotte appearance. These blue and red sashed boys have oodles of natural talent and they mean business.

Yes, funny that. Perhaps the sports outfitters in France don't stock shorts.

Though they aren't short of stocks, judging by the town squares. And after a moment's silence for the national anthem played in respect for yesterday's sad demise of Victor Mirabeau, whose two sons might well have been in opposition. Here's today's referee, Arthur Young, a thirty-seven year old journeyman scribe from Norfolkshire about to set proceedings underway. It's his first major international assignment, and listen to that noise, it really is something, you can hardly hear the whistle above the bells and horns and shouts of this capacity crowd.

The French like to enjoy their revolutions. They'll have had plenty to eat and drink, despite the reports of shortages, so let's hope today's fixture gives them something to shout about.

Straight away from the kick-off the Republicans have punted deep into the Imperial half, and de Launay evades a couple of loose tackles and off his left foot takes play back up to the half-way line. A good, secure touch.

He handled that well. It'll give him some confidence under his belt.

The two sides are sorting themselves out for the first set-piece of the match, and it looks as though the big Imperial forwards could be severely out-numbered in this department. The Republicans have the throw-in so it might go over the top. Oh dear, oh dear, a punch was thrown there, fists are flying and that's just the kind of over-physical play which disfigures and disgraces the entire game. There's no excuse for it.

They won't be taking any prisoners out there.

The referee will have to speak firmly to both packs to cut out the rough stuff. There we are, big beefy Stanislas Maillard from just down the road here, with a look saying: 'What me, ref?' Ugly bunch of fellas, aren't they?

Speak for yourself.

I was, William, I was. The language problem is going to make it extra-difficult for the inexperienced

Young, in charge of his first full major international, to prevent players from taking the law into their own hands as tempers bubble over in this seething metropolitan cauldron.

He'll have to stamp his authority upon the players right away, otherwise it could be total mayhem.

Quite a challenge for the rector's son and ex-Lavenham Public-School Wanderer. De Launay pops it up for his forwards to take it into the surging mob, hoping to break their ranks, but they run into trouble, a good firm tackle, and a heaving maul develops midfield before play stops for injuries to several of the players. Nothing is going to come out of that.

Both sides are finding their feet. Feeling each other out, probing for weaknesses. It'll be important for the Republic not to be penalised within range of the Imperial artillery, who are quite capable of plonking a ball between the uprights from several hundred yards.

The initiative still with the Imperialists, oh and a strike against the head, and Talleyrand, cleverly negotiating the attentions of those predatory breakaways, turns on a sou to put a sniping little kick down the narrow side.

That'll please his forwards.

It takes play to within a few yards of the outer perimeter, and the first real chance for the Republicans to break through. Quite a remarkable hombre, Charles-Maurice Talleyrand, who has played most of his revolutionary at inside-half. Not in the classical mold, more of a terrier and very nippy indeed for someone with a club-foot.

One of the greats. Even at fifty-one a stocky little competitor.

And out it comes on the Imperial side, and my word, that was a monstrous effort, a siege-gun boom-boom which puts the ball into touch and probably into the Seine to boot. It could take your head off. That'll rattle the chandeliers in the General Assembly, I can tell you. It brings play to midway between the Republican goal-line and their twenty-fifth amendment. He'll be chuffed with that one.

A pattern is already emerging. Marshalled by de Launay, the Imperial team are attempting to peg the Republican masses back into their own half with ranking touch-finders, before thinking of delivering a coup de grâce. On the other hand, faced with such tactics, the Republican forwards must drive in cohesively, not just ones and twos, to secure the initiative to unleash their elegant threes to attack from the deep.

And a steaming ruck has developed in the middle of the pitch, the Republican outfield lined up shallow in defence, hoping to block the attempted drop if it emerges on the Ancien side. There's a firm blast of the whistle, and it's a penalty to the Imperials for illegal use of the elbow. Nothing serious, not quite a shenanigan, just a rumbustious bit of skullduggery. 'Quieten it down, lads,' referee Young is saying.

Yes, the French always have had a weakness in temperament, giving away needless penalties, but I'm surprised he didn't play the advantage law there. As well as the drop, they could've quite easily gone over in the corner. Having said that, it's points on the board, and at the end of the day that's what counts.

You don't think they'll run it, William?

No, they must play to their strengths.

And here comes their specialist unit of mercenary guards, big Swiss fellas from Switzerland, who give the ball one heck of a thump. They have two minutes to position their howitzer, and now he takes aim, the lachrymose laddie from Lucerne steps a few paces back, cleans his studs, gives a characteristic hitch to his breeks, there he goes, and runs up. And there's a lot of ill-mannered whistling and booing from the crowd,

that's just the sort of thing we don't need. Boof. It's high enough and long enough but it's just wide.

I'm surprised they missed that opportunity. Normally the Swiss are very reliable, especially at close range, and that could have done a lot of damage to the Republican ranks, something the side with possession may later rue.

And past Rue Saint Sebastien, the Republicans take a quick twenty-fifth amendment and pile upfield. Talleyrand; Robespierre; Mirabeau; Sieyes; Robespierre on the loop before being bundled into a ditch a few paces short of the inner defences. My word, a flash of revolutionary magic and the entire tenor of the game has changed.

Quite right, Bill. There we saw French flair personified. One chink in a rock-solid defence and they were through with only the finishing pass letting them down. Perhaps Max Robespierre could have straightened up his line a little at first, but as a

snapper-up of half-chances he has no equal in the northern hemisphere.

A difficult customer to mark, the Jacobin stand-off, ever popular in his home town of Arras.

Very. Quick thinking and so elusive.

Hello, there seems to be an injury. His back's towards me, but yes, it's El Hector Thuriot, who must've been hurt in the previous melee. The players gather round and here come the Dominican Ambulance Men with the magic sponge. However he definitely still looks groggy.

Probably just an accidental clash of heads, no blood though, the question is who have they got on the bench to replace him. Immensely demanding, both physically and intellectually, top-class revolutionary turmoil.

It will require the intervention of the Court Physician to determine whether the plucky Thuriot is incapacitated. The crowd applaud the loss of the Republican full-back, who disappears, stretchered off, past the dug-outs and through the drawbridge over the moat into the mighty Bastille. Referee Young looks at his horological apparatii to blow his whistle for half-time. No score so far here at Paris and perhaps not quite living up to the crowd's expectations. Nevertheless the contest has been full of intriguing little moves which promise well for the second half. Join us then but now back to Desmond in the studio.

Thank you, Bill. Things seem to be hotting up in Paris. I wonder if the home nations might learn something from today's encounter. Elsewhere in the country, the village of Lyndhurst in Kent, before His Royal Highness King George III, has just beaten the United Kingdom All-Comers Anthem Singing Record – clear evidence that the controversial tactic of using

the updated musical arrangements by the German coach Handel has paid off, but that's not to take anything away from the Lyndhurst Choristers. Well done, lads and lasses, as a feat it must surely equal Miss Burney's mum forcing the redoubtable Doctor Johnson to drink twenty-one cups of tea in succession. Nice one, Doc. That's Johnson without a 'p' by the way, and subject to a drugs test. News is coming in of all ten states in the Italian League coming out against a Papal Decree for compulsory ID cards next season. Pius VI is quoted as saying that it is the only way to combat hooliganism and unholy subversiveness so prevalent throughout Europe. A spokesman for the League says the proposals are impractical, would result in falling gates and not solve the problem which really occurs outside the grounds. No problem with falling gates at Paris, it seems. Must be of interest to the nineteen year old Lake District striker Willie Wordsworth, whose tally last season makes him a target for several continental sides. Florence are surely firm favourites here. And just come through on the teleprinter, the result of last month's two-thirty at Wincanton is delayed due to a steward's enquiry. Later on in the programme we have real tennis and bearbaiting from the All-England Club, but now back to Paris for the second half of the Life Assurance Revolutionary Turmoil.

Thank you, Desmond. So far we've had a hard physical game, with no quarter asked for or given, but played in the best of spirits. In the second half we can expect the red and blues to open out in an attempt to free the midfield deadlock and drive deep into Ancien Régime territory.

That seems fair, Bill. The Republic undoubtedly have the talent to do well here, and so far, as the graphs show, both sides have had roughly equal possession but they've been penned in their own half by the resolute kicking of the Imperials.

So who do you think will win, William?

Touch and go. But providing they remain resolute in defence, I think the superior handling and running skills of the Republic's back division will edge it, particularly the longer the revolution goes on. But the French being the French, anything could happen.

So your money's with the French. The two teams, having fortified themselves with a half-time manifesto of oranges, line up to continue to do battle. There's been no word from the dressing room as to the condition of El Hector Thuriot, who was stretchered off at the end of the first half. The crowd don't like that one little bit, and are booing and jeering de Launay's men. Not like that in your day, Bill.

No, we just got on with it and flattened the opposition. Being a man down is a disadvantage, but it can serve to fire you up, and it seems to have got the crowd well and truly behind the Republican boys.

And so, admidst great controversy, referee Arthur Young sets this second half underway. He'll have something to write home about, I can tell you. The elder of the two Mirabeau brothers takes a safe catch from the Imperialist restart, flicks it out to Robespierre who has plenty of time to improvise a lovely little teaser which gives his wings something to chase. De Launay, perhaps slow to come across, can only run it out of play and yield the initiative. That's a cracking start for the Republic.

Yes, they'll hope to build upon this platform. The teamwork shown between Honoré Mirabeau and Max Robespierre is a delight to watch. They call Robespierre Mirabeau's monkey, but the quick understanding shown between this pair make them an extremely difficult combination to pin down, and they form a

vital link between the divergent talents of this Republican side.

And yesterday's sad death of his father doesn't seem to have affected young Honoré's game at all, does it? A fine player in his own right, he'd be proud of his son's performance this afternoon. You played against him, didn't you Bill, as a youngster?

I got his autograph once, after he took you to the cleaners at Poynder Park. I'm surprised we've not seen the younger of the two brothers, André-Boniface, perhaps his post-match drinking habits have got the better of him.

They both play for the Riqueti Club, of course, but would have been on opposite sides today. 'Barrel Mirabeau' they call André-Boniface, the human obelisk. I think the Imperialists would love to have him heaving away there because again they've lost possession on their own put-in, and it's straight out to Lafayette on the miss-move, who bursts through the centre with a dazzling declaration of the rights of man which has this tumultuous crowd screaming onto its toes. Quite magnificent, clearly his time spent training with the American Colonial side has brought an extra dimension to his game.

Most impressive, probably the best sustained piece of action of the match so far. There's still a long way to go, though, and the Republican lads mustn't lose their heads or heads could roll later on; they're not out of the wood yet, by any means.

And you saw there what an influence the great revolutionary thinkers of the past have had on today's game. 'Les Philosophes' they call them here in France. Rousseau, Montesquieu, Voltaire and Diderot, each in their own way have fostered a brand of independent enquiry and strategies to form an exciting alternative to the established orthodoxy. Odd that they've yet to make an impression the other side of the Channel.

We just flattened them and got on with it.

Meanwhile de Launay is beginning to look rather anxious here. Out-numbered if not out-gunned, he'll have to find something special to hold out against this incessant pressure and save the day.

Yes, he seems to have been somewhat hesitant throughout the game. The Ancien Régime really needed someone to impose their personality onto the proceedings and take this revolution by the scruff of the neck.

And now trotting out to join the fray inside this daunting arena comes Georges-Jacques Danton of the Club des Cordelières in place of the indisposed Thuriot. Just under thirty years of age, the attorney's son from Arcis-sur-Aube is a relative newcomer, being only the second member of his club to gain full honours, he's a bosom pal of Jean-Paul Marat, the marauding doctor, who's already out there at loose forward, prescribing some particularly bitter pills for the opposition to swallow. Georges-Jacques must be a-twitter to get hold of the ball and the pace of the game.

The Danton boy has done pretty well in provincial fixtures, I hear, and he could well consider himself unlucky to have been left out of the original line-up.

And under pressure from a scappy feed de Launay, off his weaker foot this time, tries to reach a safe haven off the field but it spirals off his boot and Danton with his first touch of the game makes a magnificent ankle-high catch, evades one tackle with a twinkling piece of oratory, sprints past the lumbering Imperial forwards with a blistering burst of scorching pace, dummies the cover, shimmies back inside, looks for support before being nailed to the cobbles a couple of inches short of the fortress gates. A real will-o-the-wisp, they'll be rejoicing in the Thirteenth Arrondissement after that, I can tell you. What a start to his revolutionary career.

Perhaps a little greedy, his inexperience showed there as he found himself forced to go wide, allowing the Ancien Régime to regroup and clear the immediate danger. But nonetheless the writing is on the wall for all to see, the Imperials will be right up against it once the Jacobin and Cordelier players combine together effectively.

It'd be a real mountain to climb. Do you think the Imperial side will be able to come back after this devastating onslaught?

Maybe a few seasons ago, but it's now more a question of lasting the pace and superior stamina with age starting to tell. The crowd are right behind the Republic so it's no surprise to see some heads begin to drop. Unless there's a real turn-around, I can't see anything other than those heads rolling as Jean-Isadore Guillotin, chairman of selectors, wields his axe in a massive clear-out.

Backs literally against the wall and fighting for their lives, they have the temporary respite of a five amendment scrummage as we enter the time allowed for stoppages. What a climax. The Republic have the put-in, Talleyrand with all his fifty-one years of experience settles his forwards as opposing front rows lock horns for possibly the last chance of the match, an almighty heave and they've won possession yet again. The crowd are willing them on, I've never heard anything like it, as they keep the Imperial breakaways sucked-in.

All sorts of options here. Down the narrow side, out to the wings, very important not to throw a loose phrase for an interception.

They must have heard you down there, Bill, because I believe they've decided to give the Ancien Régime a taste of their own medicine and go for a push-over between the posts. It's a tremendous effort and pack-leader Marat is exhorting them forward in a fury of power for one last shove as they attempt to gain purchase in their wooden shoes on the cobbles. Their opponents must remain upright otherwise they could be penalised.

As well as trampled to death.

Yes, it really is intimidating, this battering ram of awesome power, and wholly unexpected. But they're still defending doughtily, fighting hard, only they're now behind their own line, the flood-gates creak open and the Noveau Republic, their blues and reds torn and mud-stained, pour through en masse, to take the bastille by storm. Referee Young blows his whistle for the end of the game, there's no time for the conversion as the crowds invade the pitch amidst scenes of pure pandemonium. I've never seen anything quite like it. What a contest. Not high-scoring, but revolutionary turmoil at its very best. The players struggle through the throngs of rival supporters, shaking hands and exchanging jerseys, as the heroes are chaired off the field and the gallant losers trudge back to their dressing room knowing they have taken part in one of the truly memorable occasions of revolutionary history.

L'INDEPENDENT

July 15th 1789

Tunnel Vision

YESTERDAY'S EVENTS IN Paris put the preliminary discussions between the French and ourselves over a proposed Channel crossing into a different light. Scenes as witnessed outside the Bastille would not be tolerated by fare-paying members of the travelling public. Although young turks such as William Wordsworth Esq. may well be in favour of the tunnel in principle, if he were to be embroiled in a murderous mob in order to purchase a ticket, then he might well consider taking his head out of the clouds before someone else does it for him by putting it on the block. Prime Minister Pitt must intervene personally to ensure that standards of safety and comfort are not jeopardized, if the Department of Carriages and Waterways cannot come to some agreement with their French counterparts over queuing arrangements at the link's terminii. Leaving it to his Home Secretary, Leeds, to send over a bunch of cricketers is just not good enough.

L'express

DE LAUNEY LOSES NERVE

What the Papers say

LE

PRISON OFF
AT BASTILL

LE **Soleil**

PLONKEUR!

TEMPS

ERS DISPUTE

THE TAIL OF PETER RABID

by Beatrix Potash

ONCE UPON A time there were four little Rabbits and their names were:-

    Liberté,

    Egalité,

    Fraternité,

    and Rabid.

They lived with their Mother in a river-bank, underneath the cellar of a very big Conciergerie.

'Now, my dears,' said old Mrs Rabbit one morning, 'you may go into the streets or down the boulevard, but don't go into Mr Tuilerie's garden: your father had an accident there; he was put into a compote by Mrs Tuilerie. Now run along, and don't get into mischief. I am going out.'

Then old Mrs Rabbit took a basket and her knitting and went through the barricades to the baker's. They were out of brown bread so she bought six gâteaux.

Liberté, Egalité and Fraternité, who were good little bunnies, went down the boulevard to wave banners.

But Rabid, who was very naughty, ran straight away to Mr Tuilerie's garden, and squeezed under its port-cullis.

First he ate some Diderot and some English idealism; and then he ate some Voltaire; and then, feeling rather sick, he went to look for some Kant.

But round the end of a howitzer wheel, whom should he meet but Mr Tuilerie.

Mr Tuilerie was on his hands and knees planting out young dauphins, but he jumped up and ran after Rabid, waving a sharp spade and calling out 'I'll chop your head off!'

Rabid was most dreadfully frightened; he rushed all over the garden, for he had forgotten the way back to the port-cullis.

He lost one of his shoes among the dauphins, and the other shoe amongst some different sort of tomb-stones.

After losing them, he ran on four legs and went faster, so that I think he might have got away altogether if he had not run into an oubliette, and got caught by the large buttons on his jacket. It was a red, white and blue jacket with brass buttons, quite new.

Rabid gave himself up for lost, and shed big tears; but his sobs were overheard by some friendly jailbirds, who flew to him in great excitement, and implored him to exert himself.

Mr Tuilerie came up with a cauldron which he intended to pop upon the top of Rabid; but Rabid wriggled out just in time, leaving his jacket and tail behind him.

He rushed into the Arsenal, and jumped into a cannon. It would have been a beautiful thing to hide in, if it had not had so much powder in it.

Mr Tuilerie was quite sure that Rabid was some-where in the Arsenal, perhaps hidden behind some kegs of powder. He began to roll them out carefully, looking behind each.

Presently Rabid sneezed – 'Ooo, ooo, ooo, Ooo-la-la!' – spreading gun-powder everywhere. Mr Tuilerie was after him in no time.

And tried to put his boot upon Rabid, who jumped out of an arrow-slot, upsetting three piles of cannon-balls. The arrow-slot was too small for Mr Tuilerie, and he was tired of running after Rabid. He went back to his dauphins.

Rabid sat down in protest; he was out of breath and trembling with fright, and he had not the least idea which way to go. Also he was very dusty with sitting in that cannon.

After a time he began to wander about, whistling The Marseillaise through his two front teeth – but not very loud, and looking all around.

He found a door in a wall; but it was locked, and there was no room for a fat little Rabid to squeeze underneath. An old Queen Mouse was running in and out over the stone door-step, carrying cakes and cognac to her family in the palace. Rabid asked her for a drink and the way to the port-cullis, but she had such a large cake in her mouth that she would not answer. She only shook her head at him. Rabid began to cry.

Then he tried to find his way straight across the garden, but he became more and more puzzled. Presently he came to a dungeon which Mr Tuiliere kept filled with jailbirds. An ugly Swiss Tomcat was guarding them. He sat very, very still, but now and then the tips of his whiskers twitched as if alive. Rabid thought it best to go away; he had heard about Tomcats from his cousin, little Benjamin Bolshie.

He went back towards the Arsenal, but suddenly, quite close to him he heard a noise of a rack – sc-r-ritch, scratch, scratch, scritch. Rabid scuttered underneath a parapet. But presently, as nothing happened, he came out, and climbed upon a sedan chair and peeped over. The first thing he saw was Mr Tuilerie torturing a jailbird. His back was turned towards Rabid, and beyond him was the port-cullis!

Rabid got down very quietly off the sedan chair, and started running as fast as he could go, along a straight walk behind some earthworks.

Mr Tuilerie caught sight of him at the corner, but Rabid did not care. He slipped underneath the portcullis and was safe at last in the street outside the garden.

Mr Tuilerie hung up the little jacket and shoes as an example to scare the jailbirds.

But in the Arsenal the cannon-balls Rabid had dislodged rolled over one another and onto the powder from the cannon where Rabid had been hiding. There was a tremendous bang and the Arsenal disappeared.

The mice outside, hearing the noise, stormed over the walls of Mr Tuilerie's garden, demanding to see their old Queen and King. The Royal Family was frightened for their lives and asked Mr Tuilerie to find them somewhere safer and more quiet. Mr Tuilerie was quite angry about the Arsenal yet relieved none of the jailbirds had flown away in the confusion.

Rabid never stopped running or looked behind him till he got home underneath the cellar of the very big Conciergerie.

He was so tired that he flopped down upon the nice soft sand of the rabbit-hole and shut his eyes. His mother was busy cooking; she wondered what he had done with his clothes. It was the second little red, white and blue jacket and pair of shoes that the stupid blighter had lost in a fortnight!

I am sorry to say that Rabid was not very well during the evening.

His mother put him to bed and made some camembert cheese; and she gave a dose of it to Rabid!

'One table-spoonful to be taken at bed-time.'

But Liberté, Egalité and Fraternité had coke, hamburgers and french fries for supper.

✦ L'INDEPENDENT

June 30th 1791

Flights of fancy

THE FAILURE OF the dramatic intervention of King Louis XVI in the bogged-down tunnel talks will come as no surprise to readers of these columns. Doubts previously expressed as to the efficacy of the French carraigeway network proved all too well founded. The accident at Varennes, fortunate that there were no casualties, calls into question the ability of these already overstretched routeways to carry the increased traffic that will be generated by the Channel Tunnel. King Louis must return to his ministers regretting a lack of a sound investment policy earlier in his term of office, perhaps casting an envious eye over the recently completed programme of British toll-roads, where government and private enterprise have worked hand-in-glove. Thomas Telford is a wise choice to survey the London-to-Dover improvements, fitting as they do with the orbital plans to girdle the metropolis, where average traffic speeds have been the same derisory 12 miles per hour since Roman times.

LAST DAYS AT VERSAILLES
by Jeffrietta Archer

THE STORY SO FAR: *Innocent country girl Lillian Potageur seeks her fortune in the courts of Paris, and eventually becomes a hand-maiden to the Queen of France. Still young and innocent she falls madly in love with the handsome Jacques Dommage, planning to be wed that summer in Versailles. On the eve of their wedding day, the Royal family are forced to return to the capital by the raging mob. Torn between the man she adores and her devotion to the Queen and Court, she leaves a note for Jacques, hoping he will understand when they meet again in Paris. At the first opportunity she has, Lillian goes to visit Jacques but he has flown, his offices bare. Broken-hearted, she throws herself entirely into the cause of her employers, the King and Queen of France, only to see their power wane in the face of revolutionary tumult.*

The tower was gaunt and foreboding, old stone as grey as the daunting October sky between their ancient crenellations. Weary yet regal, the King Louis and his radiant Queen, Marie-Antoinette, walked past the grim turrets, the little infant Dauphin holding the hand of his proud mother. The Revolutionary Guard looked on, surly yet respectful of these commanding figures, saving the butt of their humour and muskets

for the small yet loyal royal entourage that followed in the wake of their masters.

'Mama,' said the poor bewildered Dauphin, 'why are the peasants revolting?'

'They just are. Do not ask silly questions.'

The King stood at the door, to allow us to pass through, to protect us, as best he could, from the jibe and insult of our captors. He stooped down and peered carefully at the mighty lock, as the equally mighty key turned from the outside. Once removed, a tiny shaft of sunlight, betokening our lost freedom, slipped inbetween the shadows of this drab ante-chamber.

'Louis,' said the Queen in her usual understanding tone. 'It is a perpetual shame that you only make locks as your hobby, and not also pick them.'

'I know, my cooing dove. I shall enjoy copying this one, it is the most beautiful specimen, fit for its purpose. I only hope we have the time allotted for me to complete my task.'

'You always say that.'

'One must live in hope, dearest angel of angels.'

'Yes,' remarked the Queen with a burning fire in her eyes that even I could discern in the gloomy dullness as she stared in loyal enthrallment to her steadfast husband. 'One must.'

Such a devoted and happy couple. Their constant and radiant enjoyment of one another's company, sharing of concerns, and intimate understanding brought to my mind the memory of my long-lost Jacques, the all too brief time we had spent together as one, the promises we had vowed to hold and cherish before our wedding day that was not to be.

It does not do me well to dwell upon these long days of captivity and solitude. Although my diary does say that it was only four months we spent together in that narrow tower of closeness, it seemed then to be a lifetime or more. Our captors constantly searched our

laundry and other personal belongings to see, most uncharitably, whether we had stooped to the low depths of their vulgar beliefs that we would endeavour to smuggle some billet-doux to the scattering of true and faithful supporters we possessed throughout the town and villages in this sea of troubled waters. Consequently any messages we tried to send were intercepted.

'What are you singing?'

The Queen was having her luxuriant locks combed for the eighth time that day. Her refined nose turned up at the smell of the rough luncheon they were preparing below for us to share with them. I well imagined how she felt. Cold gruel, yet again. She shook her tresses in a moment of profound irritation. Although a prisoner of her own subjects, Marie-Antoinette continued to maintain a style, grace and dignity that had made her appearance famed throughout Europe.

'A harvest tune, Your Royal Highness,' I replied, returning to my allotted task of lightly coiffeuring her magnificent tresses in search of nits.

'Well, I do wish you'd decease,' requested the Queen. 'Harvest songs are for harvests, and for peasants to sing whilst they are harvesting. Have you polished the bones of my corsets yet? And fluffed up the bustles of my dresses? Reseamed the seams of my silken stockings seamlessly? Milked the asses for my bath? Well?'

Queen Marie-Antoinette sorely missed palace life. Her size eight dancing shoes lay unfilled yet ready to step a delicate gavotte, quadrille or rondeau to the murmuring appreciation of the court. Often her performances brought them to silence, stunned as they were by her grace and elegance, and I have known her partners to retire, limping, clutching their shins and marvelling at the speed and originality of her Royal turns.

Ah, the ballrooms of Europe. I considered myself blessed that fate had given me the chance, as a simple country girl, to admire (from the servants' stairs), the dress, the fashion, the gossip and the intrigue. All most fragrantly scented with the sweetest perfumes from France's oriental colonies and spiced with the richest liqueurs that her monks and friars could concoct in praise of their worthy majesty. Small wonder that after a long night of regal duties imbibing this heady atmosphere, her imperious mistress oft became tired and emotional and her tenderly admired legs would slip beneath her as she attempted to ascend the curving staircases to retire to the celestial balcony of the night.

Yet she would refuse all offers of assistance, insistent in a faltering though firm voice that she was quite capable of climbing to the top of the marbled steps. Only when the effort became too great for her over-spent constitution did she finally fall unconscious, whereupon I, with six other hand-maidens, would hasten to carry her virtuous frame, exhausted from selfless discharge of palatial obligations, reverently and gently up to her personal wing of chambers.

Meanwhile, a cohort of footmen cleared the debris of broken Quatorze chairs and smashed urns from Sèvres, and master-craftsmen were instantly summoned from their own slumbers to repair the cracked bannisters, and replace the gilded fleurs-de-lys of the picture-frames of earlier Kings and Queens of France. Each slaved throughout the night anxious to make sure that the havoc wreaked by these unpropitious headlong descents of our esteemed and beloved Queen seemed but a mirage.

And such was her naturally humble nature, that in the late mornings afterwards, the fresh air of the palace gardens twinkling through the white and gold shutters to her boudoir, she would mention nothing of her

valiant efforts of the night before, for fear of putting us to shame with her modesty and decorum. A saint amongst queens.

She'd merely sit in the centre of her four-poster bed, fragile spine supported by a mountain of finest eiderdown freshly plucked the evening before and pillowed in scented damask. I'd carefully kneel my way the four yards across the silken covers to refill her favourite Dresden cup – a dowry present from her Austrian father – with a strong draught of black arabique coffee. Energy-drained humours replenished, she'd focus her sensitive eyes behind deep-tinted lunettes to hold her aching head sufficiently still to allow me to replace the ice she wore concealed upon her head in a delightful pompadour. The trials of royal duty.

Indeed she was so full of concern and understanding of her subjects, especially those of a meagre material station, that however mean in response their feelings may have been towards her and her family, her own in turn towards them did not alter for one instant, but remained constant and true. And though she was not French herself, Marie-Antoinette treated them as she would any others. Why, once when told that the peasants and townsfolk were, due to local difficulties largely of their own making, starving through a lack of bread, she immediately came up with a startling and novel suggestion. 'Let them eat cake,' she said.

Christmas was a drab festivity. From palaces of incalculable splendour and beauty to bare uncurtained cells. Unaccustomed to draughty corridors and damp stone, all but I suffered terribly from cold after cold. Our diet remained as mundane and as dismal as the climes and our surroundings. No change even for Noël, for the revolutionary government, if you can honour them with such a title, had seen fit to defy all Christendom and ban Christmas itself. These arrows of hurt, though they must have touched her soul, seemed only to quicken my mistress's sharp sense of humour.

only to quicken my mistress's sharp sense of humour.

'Lillian,' she snuffled as I wiped her nose. 'You must be a witch not to succumb to these colds. If I were not so indisposed and still had my rightful powers in possession, I'd have you burnt at the stake – why are you laughing, impudent child? It confirms my gravest fears.'

Thus, without a thought for herself, she attempted her utmost to raise our flagging morale, but we all knew the end was nigh. Even the infant child Dauphin had ceased to tease us with the fine sense of fun he inherited from his mother.

One wintry morning, the frost mingling with the hard-packed snow in the bare courtyard, there came a straggly motley of self-elected members of the self-proclaimed Assembly. From the battlements we gathered and we watched, the King and his Queen staring across the tumbledown chimneys and spires of their capital city, while their son, the Dauphin, playfully hurled snowballs at the haphazard group below. One of their number, blood gushing from his broken skull, fell. How were we to know that the next King of France had accidentally placed a large and sharp stone inside his innocent missile?

As comrades of the unfortunate wretch gathered about his sprawled-out body, its blood staining the snow in a cryptic message of grim foreboding, their leader looked up and I rather thought I recognised something distinctive and familiar about his dark, piercing eyes beneath his broad-brimmed hat.

'I believe they are coming for you,' the Queen said to her husband. 'Though why they are not wearing white coats is a mystery to me.'

'And why you think that they should, pearl of my eyes, is also a mystery to me. But you must have sweet reasons in your wisdom, sugar petal. Tis a pity indeed if it is as you say, for I had hoped to complete the mimic of the great lock before they took me away. You will tuck Rufus my cuddly lamb in bed at night, if I am not permitted to take him with me.'

'Of course, holding a stuffed toy will remind me of you, my liege.'

'Thank you, fairest. Now I must go.'

We followed him down the winding stairs. There was a great knocking upon the great door, which the guards ceremoniously opened. The deputation from the Assembly stepped forward and King Louis, with scarcely a glance towards us, bravely walked forwards to meet them. Their leader, his face hidden by his broad-brimmed hat, read out their orders. They were here to take their King away, for trial against fate.

The words rang out into the echoing depths of that dank ante-room which we had first seen while leaves were still on the trees – now fallen and crushed by the seasonal march of events. I glanced at Marie-Antoinette, stoic and unmoved at the departure of her beloved husband. The escort's leader continued to proclaim their perfidious imperatives from under his broad-brimmed hat.

Suddenly I recognised the voice which had seemed so familiar. My heart was mangled by a mixture of conflicting emotions, as I rushed forwards unable to help myself.

'Jacques Dommage,' I cried. 'It is you.'

There was no reply at first. Shock must also have rumbled through his manly bosom. All those memories that we still shared of our own courtship and plans, all dashed the night before our wedding feast. Honest Jacques, to see him bear my master away broke my shattered heart almost as much as it had been healed to be close to him once more. I stood aquiver. He turned to face me, and I saw that it was indeed he.

'Lillian,' he said 'I thought –'

Jacques's strong masculine arms stretched out from

his broad and mighty shoulders to hold me tighter than he had ever held me before and I was about to once again tumble like an autumn leaf into his powerful embrace, when I noticed a small diamond ring on his third finger. He was engaged to another!

'Scumbag pig,' I screamed, kneeing him in the crotch of his sans-culottes, 'and there's plenty more where that came from.'

L'INDEPENDENT

January 22nd 1793

Heady times

THE UNFORTUNATE DEATH of King Louis, whilst testing a prototype mass-exit system, will come as a shock to all Europe. Tunnel executives in France may rue their decision to make these tests public, since far from reassuring the populace, it will surely cause them to question the leadership so far shown. However the changes made during recent months in the administration of the Tunnel, are to be welcomed, bringing it more into line with the privatised enterprises this side of the Channel. Prime Minister Pitt should take comfort from this, and not allow minor hiccups to weaken his resolve. Perhaps the initiative shown by Thomas Lord in suggesting an inaugural cricket match between the two nations to celebrate the tunnel will receive a better response than the government-backed tour of four years ago which went no further than Dover.

LE Soleil

CROAKED!

D

What the Papers say

LE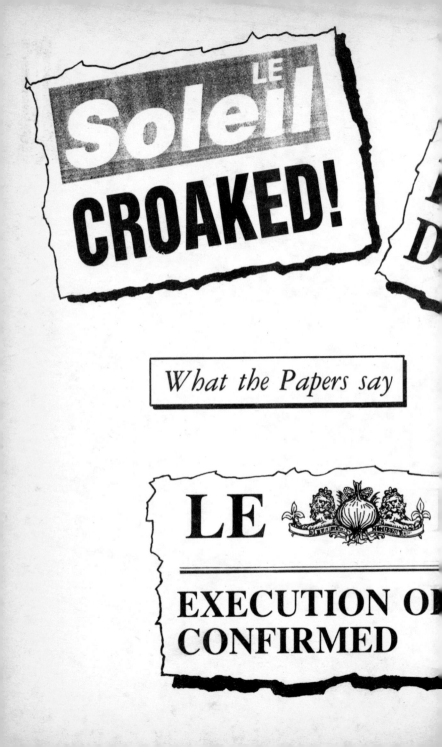

EXECUTION O
CONFIRMED

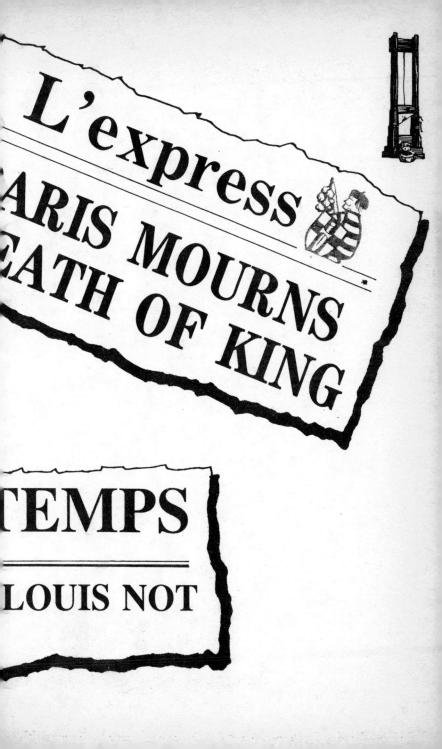

L'express

ARIS MOURNS
EATH OF KING

TEMPS

LOUIS NOT

IN THE KITCHEN WITH GEORGE AND MAX

starring George Danton and Max Robespierre

TODAY'S RECIPE IZZA fovourit in ze Robespierre 'ous'old, 'Friend's Delight.' George 'as nevur hin 'iz life 'ad ziz cooked op befure, 'av yew, George?

No, Max, I 'av nut, az yew zo rightly say. I ham lewkin furword tuit.

Ho good, mon cherry. It ez verai seemple but effectiv. Duzz wondairs fur ze constitution.

Ho, I ham zo glad to 'ear it, Max. Purraps I con try it hin ze Danton chain ov contree restaurants I av built op from werkin' 'ard fur ze Republic.

Yes. George werks very 'ard fur ze Republic han it iz luvlee to see 'im du zo well fur 'imself. I try just az 'ard az George fur ze Republic but du not zeem to du az well fur maself.

Poor Max, 'e werks zo 'ard fur ozzurs. I wandair why 'e 'as nut dun zo well fur 'imself? Purraps, Max, yew 'av nut gut arond tuit yet?

A rond tuit, George?

Yes, Max, arond tuit. Square or hoblong tuits steck to ze fryin' pun.

Han zen zey jomp intu ze fire. A verai phoney joke, George, yew meck me laff zo much.

I do?

Oil ze time. But 'Friend's Delight' iz such a seemple recipe, it weel be a joy to show yew 'ow. First yew need lotz ev wine, an' yew must giv it tu yore friend tu try. George; 'and me zat bottle I 'ave just hoepend – ho, yew 'ave drank it haul, neever mind, 'ere iz anuzzer hoepen bottle yew can try.

Zanc yew, Max. Don't mind if I du.

Hov coarse nut, mon hammy. Zen, wile yore friend trize ze wine, yew take plenti ov nozzink, boil it op huntill zere hiz nozzink left except more hor less what yew started wiz. 'Ear yew can zee a sorsepunful I 'av boiled op hurlier. Fresh plenti ov nozzink iz best but, franklee speekin', henny hold stuff will du. George, try zis bottle hov wine, it iz differen' from ze ozzerrs, it iz steel foll.

Zanc yew, Max. Are yew feelhing Hokay? Yew keep leanning from zide to zide.

Zanc yew, George, but I ham fine. Hin a leetle sorsepun, melt zum buttur han' mex it wiz zum flower to mek a roux. Yew can seizon it ef yew laike. Ma own favourit iz chilli, beycoss zis gives an hextra bite to ze dish, but du be carefol since two moch mite mek yore friend beycom 'ot hundair ze collar.

Et smells wondairfol, Maxth. I keep follin' ovair, it smellths ztho god.

Zanc yew, George. 'Ere iz anuzzer bottle yew 'av nut finessed. Now we take ze big pun ov more or less nozzink, drain ouef ze less until zere iz nozzink left but ze more, an' zen, verai carefolly wiz a woden spoon, we stir ze roux into ze more until it iz smooth, et voilà, from nozzink, we 'av a rouxmore. Wood yew laike tu try zum, George?

Thanc yew, Maxth. Hmmmmmm, it tasteths unbelievable.

Rouxmores are a specialitay ov ze Robespierre 'ousehold, yew know. Zum peephole git verai jellos han' opset beycos ov zem. Du yew know what zat Vadier said when 'e 'erd yew were hoepenink zum ov yore countree restaurants hin Paris, George?

Ham I, Max? I did nut know zat.

Hof coarse nut, mon putty. It ez honely a rouxmore, nozzing more. 'Zat Danton,' sez Vadier, 'Zat fat stuffed turbot, we'll gut him too.'

Ho, zat meks me feel verai angry an' 'ot undair ze collar, Maxth. I am nut a fat stuffed turbot, I will steck 'iz rouxmore op 'iz bum. Zen I will be more cruel than a cannibal and eat his brains. I 'ate zeze rouxmores. Yew know what 'e sez iz zo untrew, yew are ma frond.

Hof corase I am, George. What are friends four? Yew 'av nozzing to worree about. Why nut go 'ome now? Tommorrow yew mai 'av a long trial ahead ov yew. Dun't worree, I shall finnesse ouef 'ear.

Thank you, Maxth. What wood I du wizzout yew? Ho, ze top of ze dore keeps moving hup and down, joost like la guillotine. Stay still, dore, Danton iz leaving. Ho ma pore 'ed, it hertz.

Purraps yew should just lie down in ze doreway for a leetle, mon brave. Zat's ze way, George. I weel look eftair your 'ed for yew. Zweet dreams, George.

LE Soleil

LEFTIE LOONIE CROAKED IN TUB OF LOVE!

Caen charmstress Charlotte Corday last night knifed Jean-Paul Marat in the bath. Curvaceous Charlie, as she is known to her friends, told us in another exclusive: 'I did it for love – of my country. This man was a monster.'

L'INDEPENDENT

July 30th 1794

History repeats itself

CONTINUING PROBLEMS WITH the French mass-exit system leaves the travelling public ill at ease. The summary dismissal of Robespierre's team from the Committee of Public Safety does not seem to have solved their difficulties in the way that firm use of the gallows disposed of the hi-jack threats of Richard Turpin and other Kentish extremists. The plight the French find themselves in, though entirely of their own making, is not lessened by the loss of their chief scientific advisor Levasoir, and the influence exerted by the Defarge consortium seems only to be making a sow's ear from a silk purse. The Department of Carriages and Waterways will need to review operating procedures, since the revolutionary Gallic calendar may make it impossible for services to arrive on the right day, let alone on time. Assurances must be sought, and perhaps now is the moment for Premier Pitt to demand the return of the eleven days lost to the continent in 1752. Clearly a strong hand at the helm is required if the Tunnel enterprise is not to founder.

TERROR ON THE BOULEVARD
by Raymond Chandelier

NO ONE GOES out much at night unless they can help it. Death shortcuts terror the last sidewalk home. It leaves me restless, like a black cat without a tail.

For myself, I don't give a soggy baguette if people want to speak easy with cheapskate moonshine but it's bad for business. Me, I'm respectable with a reputation for honesty and truth. Straight John La Porte, private investigator.

It all started with some dame from Caen plugging Wild-Man Marat straight through the chest with the sharp end of her stiletto; him at home in his boot-shaped bath. It's not even safe to brush your teeth these days. The Wild-Man was a loud noise too, with plenty of protection. They snipped her a few days later with the big G. In public, I watched Charlotte Corday's pretty little brunette head roll into the basket. Inevitabilities like that always leave a sour taste in the mouth.

Since then even the dogs go round in pairs. Like I said it's not safe anymore. Paris is no place for the faint of heart, too easy to get it skewered, like friend Marat. My office is on the fourth floor; I don't get to see much of the cabinet maker whose shop I stroll past twice a day. Too busy turning out those one-way boxes for the big G. The mob collects them by the dozen, each box a cubit shorter than standard. The heads they stick on railings in case you miss the main event: play-back. All I hear is the tap-tap of the cabinet maker's hammer. Makes you think, particularly when you're in my business.

Feet up on the repro Louis Quatorze, I watched the rats inspect last week's groceries — salt horse on rye — before they thought better of it. Can't say I blame them, they're used to the gâteaux, quail's eggs, fancy sweetmeats of the old days when the big doubloons rolled in. Don't bite the hand that feeds you, I wanted to say, but they stopped listening to reason some while ago, like the rest of this cockaigne town. They lost their heads a long way back, too scared to think things through.

The appointments book was barer than the knees on a pair of sans-culottes. There wasn't even enough cash coming in to buy me a diary with the new calendar dreamt up by the Convention Boys at the Riding School of Tuileries. I wouldn't give it two sous for lasting, only I didn't have two sous to rub together.

Instead I played guessing games with fate, choosing which of my creditors to bounce cheques off before the big G closed the account one way or the other.

. . . Gee, I'm sorry to hear about it, Madamoiselle, your father was one hell of a guy. . . . The money? I'm just about to put it in the mail, I wish I could do more. . . . Yeh, I know how it feels, babe, it could've happened to any of us. . . .

The odds were with me, though. The Obituary Columns now came separate as a special supplement. Soon they'd have to start on the executioners and then there'd be no one left to change the faces on the railings. I tore each page out and crumpled them into the bin before hitting the next chapter of Candide.

Book of the Month Special Selection. 'In this best of all possible worlds . . . ,' I read. The rats jumped as

Voltaire scattered last week's meal-ticket into a mess of mouldy crumbs. What did old Francois-Marie Arouet know about impossible worlds? Philosophy gets remaindered when the going gets tough.

'It's open,' I snarled at the knock on the door. She was tall, high-cheekboned and corsets to match. As she unloosened her ermine wrap, I could tell she wasn't packing a rod in that bodice. She didn't need to.

'M'sieur La Porte?' she asked with a voice dressed to kill, continental, high-class, soft and slow. I could get used to dying that way, ten days a week, twice on décadi.

'Yeh, like it says on the door,' I replied. She could read too. Maybe I could interest her in some philosophy with ice, shaken not stirred. 'Always here even when I'm not.'

'Excusez-moi, je ne comprends pas.'

I shrugged my shoulders and let it go. Even I don't get my jokes sometimes. It's an occupational hazard these days, like living.

'M'sieur La Porte, yew muss 'elp me.' Her eyelashes fluttered like autumn leaves, but behind them was a cool wintry stare. 'M' 'usbond, 'e has –'

'Disappeared.'

'Ow did yew know, M'sieur La Porte?'

'It's all husbands ever do. That or chase the chamber-maid or get behind on the landau payments. Sometimes all three. Me, I prefer rats.'

'Per'aps m' 'usbond iz a rat.' Tears welled from her eyes and the orbs of her breasts swelled against her deep-cut corselette. I stopped thinking about husbands and rats, and reconsidered the erudite Voltaire. In the valley between those two fleshy doubloons seemed to lie the wordly possibilities of my kind of perfection. 'And 'e woz so nice to me.'

'Was?'

'Oui, oui, veray nice. Oh m'sieur – do yew think? Mais non, not m' petit Claude.'

After a while she stopped coughing. She had swooned – I didn't think it was my charm, and I couldn't afford deodorant – to drape herself across the chaise-longue. Like everything else in my life it had gathered dust. We waited for it to settle.

'Drink?' I unstoppered a quart of Old Musket Cleaner I'd brown-bagged from Jacques the one-eared apothecary. She took a slug as though it were Perrier without the fizz.

'Let them drink Perrier,' Copperbum Ridlée had advised the Queen in the old days. Let them. Jacques' liquor scoured the hell out of my adenoids. This dame meant business.

'O.K., Madame. When did you last see Claude?'

'M' 'usbond dus not arrive chez nous las' night. At first I wondair ef 'e wuz werking late at ze oface but az ze curfew bell tolls I beycum freightunned. Freightfolly freightunned. It ez not laike m' petit Claude.'

'So you say. Why haven't you gone to the Law?'

'Wot can zey do? 'E ez alreday undair suspicion. Hevrayone ez.'

I let it pass. The way she talked, fromage-frais wouldn't have melted in her mouth, but to make an omelette sizzle you have to crack eggs. Little Madam Claude wasn't quite ready to lay just yet, so I told myself not to kill the golden goose until money and debts went out of fashion. With her doubloons I couldn't see that happening. Counting the Thermidors since last pay day, I gave up second time round my little finger.

'Got a mug-shot?'

She looked down, hesitated, then passed across a rolled piece of canvas from out of her sequinned handbag which bulged like her corset, though in different places. I unrolled it across the imitation buckskin and shone the cheap brass oil-lamp to gain a better view.

'Yew know 'im, M'sieur La Porte?'

'Of him,' I corrected. The portrait was by some nowhere brushbender by the name of David, but I knew the face alright. Claude Rossitt was a double-entry accounts clerk to Lenses Robespierre, as Thomas Cromwell had been a shove in the Thames to Fat Harry Tudor, the divorce attorney's friend. I didn't need to be Cardinal Richelieu or the spectacles at the end of Robespierre's nose to know this was more than Junior League Boule. I smelled a rat, and looking across at my furry friends cowering in the corner, I guessed they did too. 'Ten dime a day, plus expenses.'

From between her doubloons she pulled out a wad of bluebacks.

'Keep it,' I said. 'Money won't help me find your husband any quicker.'

'Please, Jean, to 'elp uz both.' Her eyelashes did that fluttering thing again.

'Like I said, Mrs Rossitt –'

'Call me Estemé,' she implored, leaning forward across the desk to show me the contents of her safe deposit box. The buckskin drowned in the lush folds of her perfume. I didn't.

'– Ten dime a day, plus expenses. You'll get a receipt, Mrs Rossitt – one way or the other.'

'I suppose yew zinc yew air tuf.'

'No, just virile.'

She closed her ermine wrap and the oil-flame of the lamp fluttered the way her eyelashes did before. She was used to getting what she wanted. I wasn't.

'I'll be in touch,' I said. And she was gone.

I checked out all the clubs and dives where a guy like Claude Rossitt might have friends who'd talk to me. Cordeliers, Jacobin, La Gironde and The Mountain. No dice. Either they didn't know the guy or they were keeping quiet because they did.

It was a cool night. At the corner of each street the tall shadow of the big G loomed across my footsteps. Somehow I felt I was being watched, somehow I didn't feel I knew where I was going. It made two of us. The memory of Charlotte Corday seemed to echo between the shadows. I didn't want to end up a basket case; even at ten dime a day plus expenses it wasn't worth it.

'Hey, La Porte. Holà!'

I recognised the voice. Lieutenant Loufoque; we'd worked together in the old days at the Palace of Justice. All we got was grief, without a cut of the action. It had made a small splash when I left, just another ripple in a flood torrent of fear.

'Long time, no see, buddy-buddy. How's tricks down the P.J.'s office?'

'Busy,' he said, stepping out of the gloom. We kissed. Louie looked tired. 'Busy,' he said again, chewing root liquorice as though it were rope. 'Only it's no more, John. The Committee of Public Safety have hauled us all in.'

'It had to happen.'

'Yeh. Hear you're a private dick these days.'

'Sure, a godillot. Guy's gotta make a living.'

'Plenty of openings, John, if you know who to speak to in the Tuileries.'

'So I've heard. Only me and Les Halles don't see eye to eye.'

'You never did. Ten dime a day plus expenses. That's where the smart money isn't.'

'Tell my rentier. You don't know a creep called Rossitt?'

Lieutenant Lou Loufoque stopped chewing the rope.

'Rossitt? Claude Rossitt?'

He knew. He also knew he owed me for stopping a cider-crazed Breton with a sawn-off Anjou Squeezebox from blowing his face away on the Heights back in '92. Louie could've died from lead poisoning.

'Remember the Foreigner's Conspiracy?'

'So?' I replied. 'It's old stuff, Lou. Hit the fan after I threw my badge off Pont Neuf. Downtown reckoned it was a scam by Lenses Robespierre to put the finger on Pretty Boy Danton.'

'Reckon again, Bud. There's more, much more. Pretty Boy got the big G but his widow didn't collect the gelt. Fabre d'Eglantine –'

'– The guy who shafted this new calendar onto us with Deputy Romme?'

'You've got it. Played hell with the Desk Sergeant, no kidding.'

'Old Lefty. Has my sympathy.'

'Send it with a wreath, John. Rota'd himself to be two places at once last week and the Executive solved his problem. Three blocks down Rue St Martin, hang a right, twelfth railing on the left. His body's still in the morgue, they can't figure out where to hang his

long service medal for outstanding conduct in the execution of duty. Month off retirement too, poor bastard.'

'Anything to save a few sous, Loufoque.'

'Crazy but true. Dear friend d'Eglantine also cooked the Indian Contract. Word is there has to be foreign, maybe aristocratic connections. The smart money says both, only the smart money doesn't know where the real money is.'

I whistled long and low. Without realising, it started to sound like The Marseillaise. I stopped and wrung my tricorn dry of the bucket of slops some loyal citizen had chucked in our direction. I was starting to get the big picture.

'O.K. So d'Eglantine has the loot.'

'Not so fast, kid. It was too large an operation for one bimbo. He has to merchandise his territory. Not just abroad but outside the chapel.'

Notre Dame was sinking fast into a morass of corruption.

'First Baron Batz for royal backing, then Anarcharsis Cloots to arrange the pay-off out of state.'

Sinking real fast. I heard the Seine swirl around the architraves and weather-beaten statues of the infant Jesus.

'Batz is sprung. Low Countries. But we're holding Cloots on a curfew violation. He won't talk; we can't get near enough with the screws.'

'So who's the big shout behind the Foreigner's Conspiracy?' I asked. Somebody had to be. 'Come on, Lou.' Then I saw it. 'Are you kidding?' He wasn't: Louie Loufoque was too tired of life to kid anymore. 'You mean – Robespierre himself, the Incorruptible!'

'Who else? Wise up, kid, where have you been? What's he got to lose? He's Incorruptible.'

It made Richelieu look like Washington with his little axe. Richelieu was dead. The rest was easy.

'So our friend Rossitt is Lenses' bagman.'

'Or was. Give yourself a brownie point, John. If anybody asks, this conversation never happened. By the way, what does it mean when Voltaire says "Dans ce meilleur des mondes possibles?"'

That was easy. Philosophical questions always are. You can't be right so you can't be wrong. Say anything and smile. I thought about the rolled up picture in my riding cloak, the fluttering doubloons of Estemé Rossitt and the lengthening rows of railings, waiting to be emptied for the next batch of play-backs.

'It means that Voltaire knows nothing about possibilities. Nice not talking to you, Lieutenant.'

'See you around, La Porte.'

It was at the end of the last row of railings, just west of the Jardin des Plantes. The old leafless oaks gnarled over like a charnel pit of bones. An owl hooted for the dead and the dying. I saw the face I was searching for when a shadow moved behind me and I started to fall without really trying.

From the deep, from the deep. From the deep heavy locked up part of my brain oozed a thick black sound clawing to get somewhere. It hurt. Slowly, carefully I tried opening my eyes until I realised they already were. The blurs started to laugh at each other, staring into my face as the big bell kept chiselling away at my spine. I wanted to scream, then hide inside my arms but I couldn't. Nothing moved. I felt my lips grow dry yet sweaty. Terror, terror, terror.

I recognised the smell. Something soft and sweet soothed my forehead. The blurs stopped laughing and became the corners of my office. I tried waving at the rats – hiya boys, I'm back – but my arm hit me in the nose.

'Zere, zere, stay still fer mumzey.'

There ought to be a law against perfumes like that. To be broken only in emergencies. We kissed, not too

hard but not like Louie and I had earlier. Her eyelashes stopped fluttering, her long fingernails started to fool around with my shoulderblades. I felt the weight of her doubloons heave against my chest.

'Jean, Jean, O Jean. Take me.'

'Where?' She wanted me to keep still a minute ago. Her tongue danced around mine, and then she chastely let her lips peck at my cheeks. Estemé had been places, she knew all about English kissing.

'O beybay, beybay, wot 'appunned?'

'Happened.' I tried to pommade my wig but it didn't stretch over the bandages too good.

''Ear, let me. Ze door wus open and zer yew whirr, yet whirrn't, laike your joke! – O m' pauvre Jean.'

'Sure. I've walked through a door too, only it wasn't open at the time. I've news for you, Madam Rossitt. Bad news.'

'Don't tell me.'

'O.K., I won't. Anything you say.'

'Ez et m' 'usbond? 'Av yew found 'im? An' 'e ez ded!'

'Quit crying kid, it stains the carpet.'

I explained her husband's involvement with the Foreign Conspiracy. She acted dumb, but then she was a dumb blonde. Arm in arm I walked her to the edge of the Jardin des Plantes, to the railings. The rain lashed into our faces, tears from the dead. I told her about the play-backs I saw before the blackjack rolled down the curtain. From inside my riding cloak I reached for the scrap of canvas but she didn't want it back. Its colours ran, like blood, between my fingers. I could tell.

'Jean, save me. Save me from ze terreur. Zey well com te kill uz both. I know. Oui moss ron awhey from heyur.'

'Wrong, babe.' I pushed her and her doubloons aside. 'You came to me but looking for an alibi, not your husband. He was Lenses' bagman alright, but all of you each wanted more than the bagman's cut. So you and the Baron decide to fix a long vacation off limits, with you saying you'd join him later once the heat was off to avoid suspicion. Then, double-crossing the double-crossers, Claude, with your help and Batz out of the way, sells Cloots down the river, which leaves just the two of you. Only you're too greedy. Instead of fifty-fifty, first off you squeal to Mr Incorruptible, who saves the happy couple a long division sum by making you a widow, and next you come running to me, not really to find your husband but to help bale you out. There you made your one big mistake. I was good, you knew that, you needed that for the alibi, but I was too good, I got on the trail of your petit Claude for you, you get scared, arrange for Lou Loufoque to tail me so some door can rearrange the back of my skull, and while I come to, I get a free carriage ride back to my Guardian Angel.'

'Zut alors, tu as raison. Only yew whirr wrong too. I ev follen in luv wiz yew. Follin in luv wiz yew, never wonted tu, but I oilways du, cont 'elp et — Come away from zis terrible life, Jean, ze monet ez saf.'

I studied her doubloons and felt the little eyes of rats drowning in the gutter as they stared up at me. Lifebelts were usually my long suit, but I could get pulled in. Her trumpcards were soft and enticing. I was tempted, I'm human too.

'No way, kid. All I know is this. All the troubles and worries we have in this world don't amount to more than a hill of bones. Suppose we go away and live together fine and fancy free, only something might start to bother me, like a tooth the barber ain't fixed right. Bothering, nagging my mind, until I can't sleep at nights, thinking. That I might wake up and find I've cut myself shaving, with you or the big G holding the razor.'

She'd find someone else, her sort usually do until it's too late. She did, several times. We still swop postcards.

Some wise-guy stopped me on the way home that night.

'Gotta light, mac.'

'No, but I've a soaked-through riding cloak.'

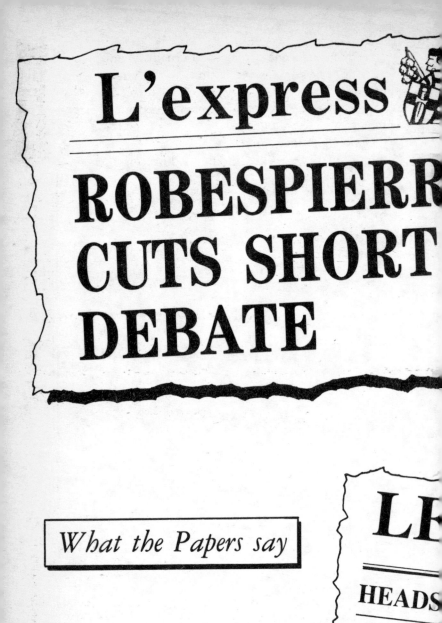

L'express

ROBESPIERR
CUTS SHORT
DEBATE

What the Papers say

LE

HEADS

MAIGRET AND THE SCARLET PIMPERNEL

by Georges Simonize

MAIGRET GRUMBLED TO himself. He was out of sorts. It was not the thick atmosphere in his tiny office, the fireplace filling the room with wafts of smoke which curled around the dense plumes from his clay pipe which he clenched between his teeth in absorbed study of his work. He could do nothing without tobacco. Nor was it the damp morning mists that had already sheathed the warped mullions of his office's squint-eyed window with a syrupy resin of condensation. Nor the rain starting to spatter down the sewers into the courtyard below. It could pour to doomsday for all he cared. The dismal clatter of horseshoes and cart wheels over shiny cobbles seemed as far away as the mounds of parchment which lay before him, like his window, unopened for years and just as mildewed with age.

The fire croaked, issuing forth yellow vapours. Another large fumey cloud escaped his lips. He slipped off the overslippers knitted for his birthday two or three years ago by Madame Maigret. A profound expression of forbearance passed across the Inspector's face. His bunions were giving him hell.

'Lucas!' he bellowed, not bothering to remove his pipe. Along the corridor came the ballet step of his assistant's feet. As a reflex Maigret leant his solid torso

across in order to poke the rheumy coals, and layers of
spent combustion filled the room to its rafters.

'Chief?'

'Drop whatever you're doing and fill the hod.'

Sergeant Lucas peered into the smoke, collided with
the desk, with his chief, the spare chair and left, his
foot as firmly wedged inside the coal hod as the clay
pipe which never left his boss's mouth. Good man,
thought Maigret, tamping down the bowl with an
experienced finger, lungfuls of ash coating the vicin-
ity. Reliable, if sometimes short-sighted.

'What's this?'

'An envelope, patron,' Lucas replied, now busily
banking up the fire.

'I know, I know.' Maigret sighed furiously. He tore
open the envelope, scanned its contents, head in a
bowl of smoke as thick as a swarm of bees. There was a
grumph, and then Lucas' delicate ears heard a crumple
of paper and the thrust of his chief's hand into a tunic
pocket. He peered at the fire's bituminous flames. The
chief often got like this, probably his bunions.

The floorboards quaked. Darkness fell upon the
sergeant's crouched form. Inspector Maigret had
hauled himself to the window, his bear-like frame
blocking any light from the courtyard outside.

'Allons, mon brave.'

Without a further word they grabbed their coats and
were off.

La Brasserie Des Aloès, as usual for this time of the
day, was empty. Mostly their business was done in the
small hours, and the type of affair which paid divi-
dends to stay just this side of the watchful eye of the
Law. Inspector Maigret burst through the door, not
bothering to read the sign which said 'Closed.' Mon-
sieur René Aloès, the proprietor, looked up and wiped
his hands clean upon his white apron.

'Bonjour, Inspecteur; Lucas.'

'Allo, Aloès. A social call.'

With years of experience, René Aloès understood. Immediately he poured out deux demis du calvados.

'Make them large,' fumed the Inspector. 'And a Langudoc sausage with plenty of mustard. Lucas?'

'Nothing for me, chief.'

Lucas eyed the helpful Aloès to leave them undisturbed, not that the warning was necessary. The three men knew one another well, it was rare for the Inspector to utter so many words at once. Something was up.

Elbows on the table he slowly filled his favourite pipe which his Sergeant, in conversation with the lower ranks, had nicknamed 'the dustbin'. Apart from having no lid, the description was just. It emerged from the Inspector's tobacco panier stuffed with great handfuls of dark perique. Thick fingers mechanically folded the envelope and the letter inside into a spall which Maigret lit from the candle which burnt between them. Its flame guttered, greasy plates hanging behind the bar shook, and cobwebs wavered as he sucked in enough air to get la grande pipe underway.

'Ministère du Terrorisme,' he growled. 'Again. Pah.'

To emphasise his feelings the second empty glass thumped the table. An instant later René was at their side, filling both from a fresh bottle.

'For yourself, Lucas? Not even a mineral water?'

'Nothing, mon patron.'

While Maigret possessed ordinary straight-forward tastes, the Parisian Lucas affected the manners and dress of the old regime. Brocaded frock-coats, embroidered shirts with ruffs and lacy cuffs, sateen breeches, shot-silk hosiery and narrow high-heeled pointed-toed court shoes whereas his Inspector preferred the stout regulation beetle-crushers. Their brass toecaps offered comfort and protection to his cursed bunions. Seeing a

gold ring glint between the lobe of the right ear and the frills of a high collar, Maigret wondered how Lucas could afford these fripperies on a sergeant's pay. Not quite one of the lads, stout Lucas, yet they still made an effective pair together, mused the Inspector affectionately before returning to the matter at hand.

'It's the Pimpernel case,' Maigret declared between puffs. 'These petit-bourgeois bureaucrats want action, not results. "Any headway," they ask, "anything to tell the Press?" They don't much understand modern policework, what they need is a good kick up the backside – Forensic Alchemy produced the goods yet?'

'Nothing, chief.'

'They've got that Walloon, Moers, on the job?'

'Last I heard, yes.'

Maigret grunted. They were all baffled. High-grade prisoners kept disappearing without trace. They had redoubled the guards, tightened up security until only the Governor of Les Invalides and Maigret knew their plans and movements. Set traps but the criminal, whoever he was, had managed to keep one vital step ahead of them. He seemed able to vanish into thin air.

The Inspector held a grudging respect for his quarry. A master of disguise and daring intelligence, leaving no clues or mistakes, and yet with a touch of humour. As the gang had fled the scene of one particularly audacious coup, their impish leader had dropped his breeches for a moment to show his pursuers in the flying squad carriage his nether flanks. There had been a large spot on his right buttock, the mark of the Scarlet Pimpernel.

They had got no closer than this. Inspector Maigret had put his best men on the case. Loyal Sergeant Lucas was always in the van, first to arrive at the scene of the crime, but even he had not been able to add to their scanty knowledge of the Pimpernel's whereabouts. What a pity Lucas had been on a well-deserved

vacation the time the flying squad had come closest to apprehending the criminal. Upon his return Lucas discovered that his chief had changed his strategy. There had to be a source from the inside, a leak. Discover that and their impertinent quarry would perhaps learn to turn the other cheek and discover what modern police methods were really up to.

'Your interrogation of the lower ranks, Lucas?'

'Nothing.'

'Dossiers? Billets des confessions?'

'Nothing.'

'La Gendarmerie?'

'Nothing.'

'Cafe gossip?'

'Nothing.'

Lucas waited in silence while the boss's adam's apple dwelled upon his sausage, drinks and pipe, hand and forearm a flying buttress to his jaw. The Inspector got like this with a case in his belly.

'What are you going to do, patron?'

'Nothing. You are going to take one of the files from my desk, dust it off, copy it out, change the names and dates a bit and have it sent to the Ministère.'

'A ruse, a trap.'

'I don't think so. Just keep them out of our hair, heh?'

Maigret wiped his lips, and after another couple for the digestion and one for the road, they rose to leave the Brasserie. René Aloès, still nursing a bruised face from a fracas involving the uniformed branch a week ago, graciously refused payment from such old and loyal customers.

'Call us what you will, you still call us in,' the Inspector gruffed in a rare moment of familiarity between all three men. 'Madame Maigret says meat is good for bruises – to bring out the swelling. I find a heavy stick generally adequate. A joke, Lucas.'

'Yes, chief.'

They walked back to the station. The Inspector liked La Brasserie Des Aloès, it was traditional, without a right angle to the place. It suited him. His sergeant stopped off at a parfumerie to buy a bottle of l'eau de Cologne. For a woman no doubt, thought Maigret. Bachelor Lucas did not drink or smoke, so the man had to have some other vices. It would serve to explain his extravagant dress-sense.

The weeks passed by but without even a perceptible change to the weather. Their investigations were nothing if not exhaustive; the corridors lay crammed full of suspects dragged off the streets, waiting days on end to be summoned into the small room down the gloomiest passage of the old draughty nick, where behind a closed door the Inspector conducted his interrogations in a painfully exact manner, the exit only ever opening for the suspect to be hauled out exhausted, beaten to submission by Maigret's methods, and back to the cells if ever needed for further questioning. He worked like a farmer ploughing a field, turning over every clod of soil again and again, pausing only to refresh himself between labours by emptying the baskets of sandwiches and bottles of calvados sent in from La Brasserie des Aloès.

They drew a blank. Maigret waited in his patient way for something to happen. Slow, resolute and purposeful. Nothing did. Perhaps the Pimpernel had gone to ground. Sergeant Lucas became taciturn, probably a tiff from his lover, the little imp had it coming to him, Maigret joked with Madame Maigret. But in his office the Inspector continued to think deeply and remorselessly, casting his mind over the problems, he himself a lumbering storm-cloud of pipe tobacco and deliberation.

He knew he was overlooking something. Something obvious yet invisible, like the stench of heavy tobacco smouldering beneath his nose. Something almost in front of his eyes, as plain as his own face. But what?

Maigret tried to get inside his man, establish his life, his every move. Dogged, the Inspector gave himself up to becoming the mind of the villain, to understand, and to know what to do next. This was Maigret's method. Pipe after pipe he smoked in rumination until he felt he knew the Pimpernel as well as he knew his own men, or himself.

The coal hod was empty. Riddling the wheezing fire in his asthmatic office, a course of action gradually hardened, as a skin at the end of his pipe-tamping finger.

'Lucas!'

'Chief?'

'Take the coal hod off your foot and listen. Get rid of that rabble outside. Tell them to go back home and behave. We'll smoke him out.'

'Who?'

'The Pimpernel. Who else? It was your idea.'

'It was?'

'Remember when you asked if I was setting a trap? Well now I am. With you as the bait.'

Sergeant Lucas tried to catch his patron's eye within the sulphurous murk.

'Listen, carefully, mon petit. You are to be arrested. We announce it to the Press. The Pimpernel comes to the rescue. Of course he succeeds. What a coup. Only you will be able to tell us his hide-out, and then –' Maigret removed his afternoon pipe from his mouth and gripped its bowl tightly between both of his huge fists. '– by Juno, we collar him. See Moers about some secret ink and invisible parchment.'

'Mais patron!'

The voice of his sergeant rose even higher than usual. Maigret remained calm and unpeturbed, a father to his men.

'I know. It will involve danger and I shall have to fetch my own coal. Do not worry upon my behalf. Sacrifices must be made in the course of duty, mon brave.'

'But –'

'Je comprends. Your friend who likes l'eau de Cologne. Don't look so surprised, Lucas, did you expect me to believe that those perfumes were for yourself? Those English lessons you say you attend at night-school? Do they dress as well as yourself in London? It's alright, I understand. Very well, I know I'm a hard man sometimes but I am not a stickler for the rulebook. It is against all regulations but tell your friend, oh, you've been transferred to the Drugs Squad at Marseilles to crack a tea-smuggling ring. Say what a bastard I am, if you like.'

'Thanks, chief.'

'Don't mention it. After that take this lettre de cachet and arrest yourself. Bon chance.'

Sergeant Lucas bowed low when Maigret suddenly errupted from his chair with an enormous roar, like a volcano, hopping at frightening speed for such a big man. There was smoke everywhere, volumes of acrid, choking gunk. Hardly able to breath, Lucas put a delicately perfumed handkerchief to his lips as the Inspector bore down on him, a crazed expression of anger transfiguring his boss's granite features.

Maigret shot past. They found him wedged in the sink, breeches round his boots, nether flanks bare as he pumped water onto their singed surfaces. Damned pipe not out, was all he would say before ordering a squad carriage home. The continual effort of gruelling weeks of painstaking interrogation had taken its toll of their chief's massively powerful frame, even down to his feet. Clearly, his bunions were still giving him hell.

'You're in one of your moods. I know.' Madame Maigret stated, quietly.

Maigret shrugged his shoulders and drained his nightcap.

'It is time for bed.'

'I am trying to finish this patch to your breeches, Maigret. If you are never going to retire, then you should at least give up those dreadful pipes of yours. No doubt you had one as a child instead of a dummy.'

'So you keep telling me, my dear.'

'Well, it only goes to show you that tobacco really is bad for your constitution. Look at your Sergeant Lucas, doesn't drink or smoke or sit at home, brooding. How is he getting along with his English lessons?'

Maigret grumphed as Madame Maigret went on. He had heard it all before.

'I am sorry that you were so bored this evening, dragging you there after a long day's work, but at least I enjoyed myself. I love to get out once in while.'

Maigret grumphed again. He could tell what was coming.

'But need you have been quite so surly, or the British Ambassador may not invite us again – or was that your idea, I wonder?'

Maigret grumphed once more and stumped upstairs. At times like this he found himself yearning for the simple days when he had first started as a detective constable and he could get on with the job, instead of attending masque balls.

If only he could send his Sergeant Lucas to them in his place. The little man would adore to be part of this mannered hauteur. Perhaps Maigret should try to obtain an introduction after this present case was over, as a reward for his brave sergeant's undercover efforts when he went behind bars tomorrow morning.

Every woman there, even Madame Maigret, had been magnetised by the presence of Sir Percy Blakeney, a heavily made-up courtier from across the Channel. Behind his masque, what did this diminutive English fop know about police-work? He was all lace and l'eau de Cologne. A dandy, a ladies' man, more like this woman which Sergeant Lucas kept quiet about, or Lucas himself, for that matter. They both wore a gold ring in their right ear, for what it was worth.

Why, in the gentleman's cloakroom Sir Percy had put his hand upon the Inspector's singed flanks, and only the bother of international law had stopped Maigret from clapping the elegant Englishman in irons on the spot. Some strange feeling had told him that the Scarlet Pimpernel was almost in his grasp as Sir Percy had pranced away. They were that close to completing the case. What had this social parasite said? Ah oui.

'Luck as becomes the hare and the quarry, n'est-ce pas, Inspecteur? You'd already know your man, if only you knew it?'

Pah. Riddles of jesting nonsense. All Paris seemed to be laughing at the Inspector, even this foreigner Blakeney. Eyes heavy-lidded, Maigret tried to construct a picture of the Scarlet Pimpernel from the one scrap of eye-witness evidence – the spot.

This mental portrait was the only real picture of the man which Maigret possessed, and in theory it was good enough, but now it was replaced by fleeting images which should have added up to one and the same man but which refused to get themselves to focus. There was just a masque between the Pimpernel and the Inspector.

Maigret grumbled to himself. He would nab the villain. With Lucas arrested, he was sure of it. Tomorrow evening he would visit La Brasserie des Aloès for his usual demi before going home. He and René would talk about the latest sensational jailbreak reported in the evening papers. His lips intoned these thoughts as he finally fell asleep that night.

'We seek him here,
We seek him there.
We seek the elusive Pimpernel
Everywhere!'

L' INDEPENDENT

October 7th 1795

A Whiff of Good Sense

WORRIED TUNNEL SHARE-HOLDERS on both sides of the Channel will breathe more easily after the extra-ordinary meetings in Paris last week. At long last the French government has acted with a firm hand and brought their side of the enterprise into good order. Not just the friends of France, but the whole of Europe will be pleased with the display of coolness and sagacity shown by the young Corsican Napoleon Bonaparte in sorting out those who can only be

described as trouble-makers. He brings a military precision to proceedings and promises to provide a long overdue up-date to the antiquated French carriageway-network. Work at the Dover end of the Tunnel can now continue in an atmosphere of peace and good will, with the forthcoming Test Match next season between England and France being a fitting celebration for an enterprise which, over the years, has had more than its fair share of difficulties.

BALL BY BOULE COMMENTARY

RBC Radio 3 coverage of the First Test

GOOD AFTERNOON, AND we welcome Colonial Service listeners to the Channel Tunnel with the gloomy news that no play has been possible since tea due to bad light. In fact the umpires offered it to the batsmen just after lunch, but it was so dark no one realised until the tea interval. As I look out of our commentary box high above the Straits of Dover, I have to say that I can't see the situation improving. On the square itself, in the centre of the tunnel, it is absolutely black. What do you think, Fred?

The square itself

Oh aye, not brilliant but played in worse, much worse. Can't see what's all fuss's about, really.

And our other seasoned expert, Trevor Braintree?

I'm not sure I'd like to agree with Fred completely. Somehow I can't see how the light could be worse if it's already pitch-black. The pitch, incidentally, is looking rather splendid, if you were able to see it. Naturally, if this were an ordinary village game and not a Test Match then they'd still be out there playing, without a shadow of a doubt. Although it must be very difficult for the batsmen to see the ball in the dark, it's pretty much the same for the fielding side, and it's such a shame for the capacity crowd. Spectators have paid a lot of money to be here today and if play were to resume now, then they'd not be able to see a thing, of course. Perhaps they really should think of giving it a go. After all, the light, Jonners, can only improve.

Thank you, Trevor. Batsmen at the White Cliff Road end of the ground are, of course, without the benefit of these wonderful sightscreens below us, chiselled away from the gently sloping chalk by the tunnel contractors especially for this occasion. There was a little bit of dampness on the bowlers' run-ups where a spot of sea-water had seeped through the covers, but play started on time with the French team winning the toss, and electing to take the field. It's the first time these two countries have played each other, so let me just run through the scorecard so far.

England. First Innings.

Wellesley A ....not out 0
Nelson H ....not out 0

extras: byes, 0; leg-byes 0; wides 0; no balls 343
Total 343 for 0

A steady beginning, Fred?

Not bad, not bad. Building a base, nothing spectacular, liked to have seen Sir Geoffrey at the crease though, to accelerate the scoring a bit. Of course they're both playing for their places, if they don't do well here then it could be the boat to Australia for the pair of them.

What do you think, Trevor?

I'm still a little worried about the running between the wickets. It's a longer than usual pitch — twenty-two leagues rather than yards — and I can't help feeling that they might have trouble in judging the ones and twos necessary to push the score along against this deep-set French field. Particularly young Nelson's tendency to turn a blind eye to the quick signal. Which, incidentally, can't help him in light like this. I think we should remember that, if at times he's seemed marooned at the far end of the pitch.

Yes, he almost came unstuck against the Danes at Copenhagen, didn't he?

Ah, but that was a rather different situation. A heck of a sticky wicket, either hit out or be out, and he hit out, very effectively, by all accounts. Whereas the pitch that Head Groundsman Tom Lord has prepared here is a pretty near perfect: straight and true, perhaps lacking a little in bounce, with the ball coming though rather low, making it difficult for the batsmen to play their shots.

Fred, you don't think that could be accounted for by the heavier French Boule?

I've always said line and length, pitch it up and ball'll do rest. All this rolling ball along the ground, can't see what these Frenchies are up to, don't understand it myself. Line and length, like I've always said. They should pitch ball right up. Make the batsmen play. Funny game, though, cricket. You never know, anything could happen.

And I've just been told by the Wigless Wonder, our

tame statistician, that there is a dispute between the French and English scorers.

Yes, it concerns the number of no-balls bowled, if that is, you can bowl a no-ball. As the French employ boules and not balls, the English Scorers have taken the view that they are not bowled but bouled, and therefore are no-balls, which accounts for the total of 343, whereas the French, used to playing with boules and not balls, consider their boules to be balls, and not no-balls when bowled, or bouled. Their no-ball, or no-boule total is none, which leaves a discrepancy of 343.00. I might add that this is the longest time in any cricket match whatsoever when nothing of interest has occurred. It beats the previous record of Sisyphus, of the Old Corinthians who carried his bat and stonewalled out the match in Hades.

Thank you, Wiggers. Have a piece of chocolate cake and shut up.

Boules, bowls, all sounds to me like a load of old –

Yes, Fred. Here we have a very interesting letter from one of our listeners, a Miss Jane Austen of Bath:-

'Dear Test Match Special,
One half of the world cannot understand the pleasures of the other, yet you have delighted us long enough. A lady's imagination is very rapid; it jumps from cover to slip, from slip to deep gulley in a moment. How can you contrive to sound so even?'

Well, thank you very much, Miss Austen, we do do our best to please. Oops, there's a P.S.:-

'One cannot be always laughing at a man without now and then stumbling upon something witty.'

Funny you should read out that letter, Jonners, because Miss Austen is dead right. Cricket, as I keep saying, is a very funny game. Anything could happen.

What's the funniest thing that's happened to you, Frederick?

Oh, has to be at Combined Services a few year back. The young lad Horatio was at wicket, and score reached 111. 'Why that's Nelson,' I says, 'One arm, one eye and one –'

For the record book. I'm sure Miss Austen will appreciate your expert comments, Fred, wherever she's listening. Late switchers-on will be intrigued by the large number of bats broken today. I've never seen anything quite like it, particularly against the medium-pacers. The boules seemed to splinter the willow into smithereens.

Can't get the wood, you know. You just cannot get the wood. I was talking to Cruns, who are undoubtedly the makers of the toughest bats to be had, and they were saying the same. Oh Mister Fred, they said, you can't get the wood, you know.

I think I'd agree with Fred up to a point, but much depends upon the pace of delivery. Anything which is around about fast-slow-medium is liable to do something.

Trevor, it was interesting to see the French players take the field attired in helmets and military uniforms, rather than caps and white flannels.

They seem to have adopted a more cautious approach to the game. Played properly, if any parents of young children are listening, cricket is very safe and a tremendous builder of character. You only have to watch Arthur Wellesley at the wicket, the Iron Duke as they call him, and a product of the playing fields of Eton. Personally I'd find helmets an irrelevance.

Trevor's speaking from long years of experience, you know. There's only one place on cricket field I'd wear a helmet and normally it doesn't show – remember when I caught you in the Nelson's at Scarborough?

Yes, Fred, I do.

Line and length, that's what I always say. Line and length. Ball'll do rest. Perfectly safe game.

King George II's son, Frederick, died a little less than half a century ago in 1751 after being hit by a cricket ball.

Shut up, Wigless, or Fred'll throw you and your record book out to the seagulls. And Trevor, what did you feel in your playing days? About being hit?

A certain numbness, on the whole. I have to say that you could shake up an unprepared batsman with a boule fired in early. I'm sure that's in part why the French have chosen Bonaparte as their captain, even though he is a professional.

Yes, Nappers will be keen to get on with the game, as boule is a national sport and he now has the nation behind him. What do you think the tactics of two teams will be if play does resume?

Oh, bat out till stumps without losing a man, I should think.

And if, God forbid, Trevor, one of these two were to go, would you send in a nightwatchman?

In this light, definitely.

Fred?

I'm not going out there, light like this, mug's game. You two must think I'm barmy.

Well yes. Perhaps it's time to call in our guest commentator, Maurice Chevalier, for his view.

Thank heavens for little boules,
They make the English give up before May,
Thank heavens for little boules,
They force them to retreat in disarray.
Against the light they always try appealing,
While we send their balls crashing through the
   ceiling.

Interesting you should say that, Maurice, we've just heard that the covers to the tunnel have collapsed completely, and as well as bad light, the pitch is now under 76 – thank you, Wigless, 77 fathoms of water. That would rather seem to put the dampers on play for today, though as Fred said, cricket is a funny game and anything could happen. What a miserable summer this has been. Sorry Trevor, you were going to say something?

Unless, of course, they had some diving suits handy. Even so it would make things difficult for the fielding side having to play with such a slippery ball, or boule.

It also means that this Sunday's charity game in the fields of Kent where the Yeomen of England play the French Army may have to be postponed. As indeed might the whole French Army's forthcoming tour of the Counties. Which would be a great shame since we've not had a touring side visit these shores since –

– 1066, the Norman side brought over by William the Conqueror, who remaining undefeated after winning the First Test by an innings, after the English captain Harold was forced to retire dead with something in his eye.

Thank you, Wiggers. Rather different sort of game now, of course. Any comments? Trevor? Maurice? Fred?

Pity really. Big crowd. Calls into question the whole idea of permantly covered pitches, I suppose.

Thank heavens for Fred and Trev,
They talk of nothing every summer day
Thank heavens for . . .

My Crun Jumbo Sledgehammer shut him up. Funny game, cricket. Anything could happen.

And nothing usually does. Listeners can probably just about hear the Town Crier announce that play has been officially abandoned for the day, and that if they can mop up the Channel in the meanwhile, there should be a tunnel inspection first thing in the morning. With that sad news from Dover, we return you to the Studio to join a selection of popular tunes, starting with, appropriately enough, Handel's Water Music.

LE Soleil

WHAT A WALLIE, WILLIE!

NEWS SPECIAL

Cloth-eared Cockermouth rhymster wrote out today in favour of the French Revolution. Who are you trying to kid? Just watch it matey, or more than your Arts Council grant could be for the chopper.

'Go back to the Lakes and bleat it to the sheep,' says Blunt Blank Verse, The Sun's Top Ten Tipster. 'What a buncha daffs! You couldn't even complete a couplet for a Crazyfarm Christmas Card.'

127

THE MOLE WHO CAME OUT OF THE GROUND

by John le Carrot

WAS THE ROMANTIC era so romantic? Le Observateur Revue brings to you an exclusive extract from the latest work of the master of the English spy-novel, set almost two centuries ago.

George Surly kept the scarf around his neck. Watchet was windswept early autumn cold, and the long ride from London had left him chill and unsettled. The inn-keeper's wife laid out the rude trestle from. 'For two, please,' ordered Surly, 'I am expecting a companion, you understand,' he added, perhaps unnecessarily.

Too many things were out of place. Free Trade was now off-limits; Revenue had declared itself bankrupt; Colonial Office still reeled after recent losses; Paris Station had lost its head; Royalty seemed to be mad and the Fat Controller was not pleased. Surly peered into his goblet of dark Madeira and wondered to himself. He was right; he needed to be closer to the events, sense their reality to obtain a clearer picture. Like a Beethoven piano sonata at the start of his late phase, London was becoming a town too full of impressions: divorced metaphysically from the nation; deaf to performance. The grandfather clock by the inglenook ticked to itself like a metronome.

'Good evening, Porlock. Do sit down.'

'Thank 'ee kindly, squire,' replied Surly's guest, his ageless weatherbeaten features in sharp contradiction to his host's more urbane appearance. Porlock was one of their most experienced field operatives. 'Farmers' they were called inside Whitehall. Farmer Porlock was slow but dependable.

'You may dispense with the accent.'

'What accent?' Porlock replied. 'This is how I talks natural, like.'

'So I gather.' Surly paused. Under the small table he was worried lest they trod on one another's toes; or drifted too far apart from each other. In the somulent yet mysterious Valley of Stones between the Brendon and Quantock Hills, Farmer Porlock was George Surly's eyes. 'Tell me all you know about the Pastoral Movement.'

'Well, the sheep go up in the hills during summer and back down in the valleys come winter,' replied Porlock. 'And that's about all there is to know.'

George Surly remained silent and unamused; he had not journeyed so far to discuss old wives' tales; there were enough of those behind desks inside Whitehall. He listened to the inn-keeper riddle the gutteral fire and Porlock clear his throat; the sounds twisted around each other in his mind, an old familiar knocking from within. 'I'll have you, I'll have you,' it ordered, a schoolmaster's voice. 'I'll have you.' But who? Who? Everybody, supposed Surly, when just as suddenly the stream of consciousness ran dry.

'You alright? Look's though ghost gorn and crossed your grave.'

'No doubt, Porlock, no doubt. As you were saying; the Pastoral Movement. Wordsworth.'

'Odd blighter. Keeps wandering off into fields, and staring at daffodils. Funny, like I said, but mostly harmless.'

'He didn't see you?'

'Oh no, disguised myself as a scarecrow, didn't I, squire. As it says in the manual. Works everytime.'

Porlock's farmcraft was gospel in the Monastery. A catechism to Novices. He may have been a Franciscan Monk to the Cardinals of Pall Mall, but here he was a master in his element. Yet had Porlock defected to another order, and what if he had? Surly felt himself as lost and as out of place as a sexton at the Ka'aba of Mecca. Holy of holies, his work had taken him throughout the empire, but he had no experience of its provinces. O foreign lands; unknown.

'Go on.'

'That's all there is, squire. There be nothing else *to* go on. No dead letters, no safe cottages. If you want my opinion, Wordsworth's a funny blighter, but he's no Frenchie's spy.'

'Thank you, Porlock. If you would keep to what you saw.'

'Well, he do write a lot of letters, and poems, and things.'

Surly winced. The accent was bad enough, the grammar and vocabulary were simply atrocious; so ordinary and uneducated. Continental orders would shun him, only the English were so egalitarian, or desperate. Porlock was best left in the field; if he were to come to London, the class-conscious Rural Desk would crucify him alive.

'Porlock, you say Wordsworth did not see you.' Surly was careful to keep his voice neutral yet welcoming; a father at confessional, a shepherd to his flock. Porlock examined his square-shaped fingernails; each hardened hand a remorseless unthinking mawl. Surly continued, in the tone of absolution. 'Witchhunters intercepted a message to Wordsworth's sister expressing how they seemed to be watched from afar. Are you sure they did not see you?'

'That'd be Walsh, one of Portland's boys. Them Home Office buggers haven't a clue; they stick out like a mangel-wurzel in a turnip field. Tell 'em to bugger off.'

'The matter is outside my jurisdiction, Porlock, but I shall intimate your concern.'

'Not the same as tellin' 'em to bugger off.'

'No, it is not. You realise your mostly harmless scribbler is on record as being a supporter of the French Revolution.'

'And you backed Humor & Rumor that the King of England is as daft as a nun's shaving-brush, Mister Surly.'

How did Porlock know? It was top-level classified information; only the whole of London was aware of it. Where was the link? It lay somewhere, somewhere between the shores of Porlock, Watchet and the Valley of Stones. 'I'll have you,' repeated the voice, more insistent this time. 'I'll have you', as though shouting at his wife to open the door when he had forgotten his latch key. 'I'll have you.' There was something they had all forgotten.

'Bill's mate Sam might interest you, though.'

'Sam?'

'Coleridge Taylor. He's another funny one, he is. Partial to the laudanum, very partial. I'd have thought you'd know about him, Medical Records being what it is. Most kind, squire.' Porlock put his empty ale mug down in front of Surly.

Medical records were in the habit of being lost; that was how they were kept confidential. Surly ordered another ale for Porlock and a Spa Water from Bath for himself.

'They'll give you a hoick from the pump. Don't know any different, they do, not knowing what a bath is. Old Coleridge Taylor came unstuck that way.'

'Really now.'

'Oh yes. Orders this Spa Water stuff, landlord gives him last week's run-off from the pickling-barrel, and ten minutes later, after waxing lyrical upon the goodness of rustic life, is took poor with dysentry. Proper colly-wobbled, he was – you've not touched your drink, Mister Surly.'

'I'm – I'm letting it settle. Do go on, if you will.'

'I sees my chance, don't I? Drops by after closing time, reckoning, with the drugs and gippy gut and all, he might like a bit of company, like, and I catches him in the act.'

'Of what?' requested Surly. 'Spare me the exact details if they are too — gruesome.'

'Gruesome? Poetry ain't gruesome, is it Mister Surly? Personally I think it's plain daft. In my book, only thing it does do is stop them what's daft enough to write it in the first place going any more dafter. Me, I prefer a simple game of cricket. There's no accounting for tastes.'

'No, there is not. Mister Porlock, I do not suppose that you managed to obtain a copy of this poem?'

Porlock stared straight across at Surly: eyes laden with anger, pride and hurt.

'Mister George Surly doesn't think I can read and write, does he?'

Surly donned a pair of half-rimmed spectacles and stared down at the scraps of paper that Porlock had thrust across the table. He tried to avoid his own embarrassment. Porlock was right; George Surly had believed that he was illiterate.

'There's probably more, but I think my dog might have staunched the daft twassock in his flow. Talking of which, I've got to shake hands with your wife's best friend.'

Too busy reading, avoiding social embarrassment to pay attention, Surly did not look up but intoned the lines to himself, over and over again. On the surface it was nonsense, opium-crazed nonsense, but that was only the surface, the impression deliberately obscure upon the creased page. There was a message, if only he could find it.

He cursed Porlock for interrupting Samuel Taylor Coleridge. Who was Kubla? Who was Kubla in the Valley of Stones? In all the lines of verse, letters, correspondence, minutes, meetings, registers and commentaries they had bugged and burgled their way through to lose in the basement depths of their hallowed filing system, there had never been a mention of Kubla. George Surly knew it was important, particularly if it did not exist.

Ordering a pipe of finest poppy-seed, he drew from the verse for the last time. From beginning to end, he knew the whole thesis was wrong.

Nothing worked, nothing interlocked, nothing explained the *poetry*, nothing explained itself. He had constructed a chain of which no one link was capable of supporting the others. Holding his head, he let the Furies loose and watched them posture in grotesque slow motion before his tired imagination: Kubla was a person, as real as the Spa Water he had just sipped. Can he – or she – have been the link they were searching for?

Certain phrases fell into place; pieces of a jig-saw puzzle that had no edges.

> '*Through wood and dale the sacred river ran,*
> *Then reached the caverns measureless to man,*
> *And sank in tumult to a lifeless ocean:*
> *And 'mid this tumult Kubla heard from far*
> *Ancestral voices prophesying war!*'

George Surly understood. A reference to the flooding of the Channel Tunnel during the First and Last Test Match. The French had blamed English

THE COMPLETE GUIDE TO THE FRENCH REVOLUTION

135

craftsmanship, the English French, and with each fall of arches had crumbled relations between Westminster and Les Tuileries. But here was a reference to sabotage in an attempt to precipitate a conflict that would tear the Bayeux Curtain to shreds, and disclose a field of combat played to the death. His old schoolmaster stood over him, bowling googlies. 'I'll have you, I have you.'

The Duke of Portland's men at the Home Office were right: they would have to call in these two so-called poets; interrogate them till their souls were bled white. Fat Controller's Leeches frightened George Surly at times. He would summon Especial Branch in the morrow. Issue warrants to rescind their poetic licences.

'Well, I'm off, squire. Moles keep buggering up the village cricket pitch and night's the right time to catch the little buggers. Coobler's very handy at it.'

'Kubla?'

'That's right, Coobler, my dog. Can sniff 'em out of their tunnels like nobody's business, clever little bitch.'

George Surly scarcely listened; he needed more evidence. Before retiring for the night, he took a fresh quill and wrote it.

I wandered lonely as a burr
That clings to coats of toffs and swells,
When all at once I saw the nerve,
The brass, of Frenchy ne'er-do-wells;
On the take, from a bourgeoisie
That yields estate to fleurs-de-lys.

Humble garbed in sans-culottes,
The peasants sweep the gutters free;
Then brushes raised, they show their bots
To the local constabul'ry.
Ten thousand I saw at a glance
Drop their kecks in the name of France.

Laced fops before them fled; yet they
Out ran those silk calves easily.
A poet could not but be fey,
Amidst such peasant company:
I dreamt – and dreamt – and, gosh, big thought,
What wealth this scene to me has brought:

Sometimes, whilst on my tod I pause
In squiffy or in spaced-out mood.
Heads roll without effect or cause
To catch the bliss of solitude;
And then my brain with query fills,
To proclaim the end of social ills.

WILLIAM WORDLESS

L' INDEPENDENT

November 22nd 1797

The best of lines and the worst of lines

THE FAILURE OF France to come to terms with modern political and economic realities will leave the rest of Europe cut off from the mainland. More than a cricket match was left undecided two seasons ago when a water-logged pitch caused the fixture to be abandoned. Tunnel contractors are still as bogged deep in bureaucracy as the workings themselves are now in seaweed. The English precondition of refusal of entry of garlic, frog's legs and edible snails is reasonable: Customs and Excise at Dover have strict quarantine regulations to uphold and the majority of the British public would be appalled to see foulbreathed creatures hopping and crawling around the place. Already one of these has been sighted in Hartlepool, and are we to trust the French Embassy's explanation of an escaped ship's monkey?

Spying is a serious matter, and though this paper is the first to defend free speech, we applaud the Home Secretary's decision to empower the constabulary to imprison anyone who rhymes without holding a valid poetic licence. An unattributable source, Mr Bonehead Press-Secretary, told this paper that a potential poet laureate is involved in these spy scandals. The risks to national security are as massive as the top-secret Martello towers built to protect seaside towns from the prying eyes of French day-trippers. It also, of course, shows our secret service to be as watertight as the Channel Tunnel after it sprung its last leak. The cabinet may soon have another Nell Gwynn blow up in their faces.

Perhaps now that Napoleon is more interested in having his portrait hanging in all the capitals of Europe, we should reconsider the high-speed carriageway from Dover to the capital. More of this will be underground than the tunnel was itself, so why not bury the whole lot and forget about it?

LE TOUR DE FRANCE
TV World Inaction

AND AS YOU can see from the overhead balloon the crowds are all along the Champs Elysees waiting to cheer the winner home. The race carriages have just come into view on this, the last stage of the inaugural Tour de France. And here he is, wearing the coveted leader's red tunic, looking very relaxed indeed after a gruelling campaign, the wily Corsican, Napoleon Bonaparte. The rest of the field are nowhere as he enters Le Cours la Reine, a wave to his supporters before putting one hand into his tunic with that characteristic riding style of his – if he were to have a puncture now, I'm sure he'd feel a right tit. With me is Jo-Jo Sarfinn, the Swedish Raleigh Champion.

Fantastic. He has done very well. Could take all Europe by storm. Particularly strong at grinding the opposition down with deep attacks. Maestro in the saddle.

Yes, he showed that early on by masterminding the French team's victory at Toulon, already a big gun then, and he's capitalised upon that success taking the King of the Mountains title from a confident Italian field.

His bandy legs are ideal for those tortuous climbs. And of course, he is totally devoted to becoming number one.

That shows in how he has dictated proceedings throughout this marathon event. There's probably not a man in Europe who can match him at the moment. The spectators are overjoyed as he can just see the Palais Royal and the sight of victory. I have to say that he makes it look so easy, not a drop of sweat after beating the opposition completely into the ground. It's not yet been confirmed but if he does win then the First Consulate could be his for the asking. What an achievement for a man his fans call Le Petit Corporal. He crosses the line now, arms raised in triumph, with a record-breaking time. And after the break, we'll be going over to Jo-Jo for A World Inaction exclusive interview.

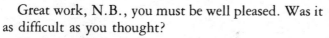

Great work, N.B., you must be well pleased. Was it as difficult as you thought?

No, not really.

And your plans? Today France, tomorrow the World?

Ask me tomorrow.

So you're going to be celebrating?

Not tonight, Jo Sarfinn.

NAPOLEON

~~Robespierre~~

~~DANTON~~

~~MIRABEAU~~

RULES

ABSOLUMENT

VIVE LA REVOLUTION
by David Fine

HER EVERY VILLAGE has a village hall. Every April the colours of Spring and her trumpet-shaped flowers summon the villagers from their daily travails and up into dusty lofts, down dark cellars and then, well-shadowed in the early evening light, proud figures they stride purposefully across the square carrying strangely packaged shapes into the unlit hall.

The pack of wild dogs in the hills stops howling. The pigs in the back-yards give up the grunt at uppity chicks. The barkeeper clears the tables and corks the open bottles of wine behind the bar, then unplugs le juke-box. The lads at the pinball machine watch the last ball miss the last pin and go down. The old woman who runs the shop turns her old transistor radio off, and the children cease scragging each other on their silly looking BMX bicycles to stare towards the hall, the eyes of a nation. All is still, all is silent.

Not for long.

Imagine that atoms were notes, and when clustered together, they made tunes, in a divine theory of harmonics. Were this true, then the noise bursting from the hall is an atomic bomb going off. The disintegration of music releasing shockwaves of sound to numb all sensibilities. The removal of light-bulbs from the hall is a precautionary measure against shrapnel and worse. This is first practice of the village band in preparation for July 14th. They do not get any better.

The seasoned listener can in fact discern the initial swish of the leader's baton going up and then down like the handle of a detonator. Having served its purpose the baton is thereafter ignored, and all contact with the world of music is severed. The aim of the exercise is to extrude from each instrument as much noise as possible, and as one particular player in the lead tires or falls through strain, another takes over, rather like a Grand Prix race where different timbres of exhausts jockey, overtake and lap one another, but they can never play in unison. Pitstops for refuelling or tyre changes are permitted, but there is no escape from noise. Cymbals clang like dustbin-lids; drums beat like Thor and Woden on piece-rate; brass, woodwinds and monstrous euphonia rent the air with blares, squeaks, shrieks and oompah-pah-pahs. So thus the rented air is shredded, mangled, crunched and scattered into little pieces far and wide.

It makes the entire Notting Hill Carnival backed by the New Orleans Mardi Gras and the Last Gay Whales Rock Against Racism Heavy Metal Concert sound softer than the Lindsay String Quartet, pianissimo. There is no relationship to music whatsoever. Not even random, let alone co-incidental. How could there be? Everyone knows enough monkeys with enough time and enough paper — together with enough money — shoved through enough typewriters could, in the end, piece together Hamlet; they wouldn't be journalists otherwise. But these bands can't even produce one note of music, they are all out of tune, but never in tune with each other's out of tune, if you know what I mean.

This requires something, a very special something, which is neither luck nor skill. Uri Geller bending spoons dulls by comparison. It beggars understanding. Yet however much the village band bangs, booms and blares, you know and they know that nothing even Schonburg or Cage would allow as music will ever caress the air. Just the opening bars of Beethoven's Fifth is an impossible dream, these players are tone-deaf inside their heads. They do not care: to produce music is not their purpose. Quite the opposite.

To belong to the band is a great honour, duty and obligation. L'ésprit de la Revolution may be carried in the hearts of all their compatriots, but it is expressed through their fingers, embouchures and lungs. They take their responsibilities seriously. Every week they practise together, gaining in strength and stamina, in readiness for the great day. For the sensitive outsider there is scant consolation in the datum that they do not get worse. They cannot. It is the final stage in melodic entropy; from heavenly choirs the earth has decayed to sibliant chaos. The village band does not get any better, just louder.

Added to their banging and crashings are the thumps and thuds of bits of plaster and masonry falling from the ceiling and walls of the hall. Flakes of rusted cast-iron ping in metallic hysteris from the public urinal outside. Mirrors crack, doors jam, cabinets keel over and foundations of adjacent dwellings subside. Jehovah would have signed them up on the spot.

Insurance officials shrug their gallic shoulders to authorise claims of damage due to revolutionary activity. Year in, year out, the premiums go up as the buildings fall down. No need to make a crisis out of a drama, nor much of a loss either.

The great day beckons and the tempo hots up. Nightly the village quivers to caterwauling quavers. Macbeth doth murder sleep, these anti-royalists commit genocide.

Flags, buntings, rosettes, banners and festive decoration transform the pastel shades of what little remains of the village into a rich collage of colour. Every window and doorway is open and filled with expectant faces as are lined each side of the street. They wait in silence. As though from afar comes a familiar sound, and suddenly, errupting into daylight, the band bursts from the confines of the shuddering hall.

It is the most stirring and splendid spectacle to behold. Somehow it is noble, glorious and magnificent. It all makes sense. It touches the heart, the soul and frees the intellect to attain dizzying heights. It makes you want to embrace your neighbour and they you.

It is the revolution.

Vive la Revolution!

1789 AND ALL THAT

QUIZ

PRIZES WILL BE awarded for sycophantic originality at the discretion of the Sunday Colorsupp Newspaper Group plc. Only their employees and relatives may enter. Anyone found cheating with garlic will be beheaded by the Committee of Public Safety.

1. *L'Ancien Régime* was replaced by:-
   [1] Beaujoloais Nouveau [2] Oral Contraceptives [3] The Post-Modernist Movement.

2. The Third Estate was the first people's motorcar. Did it go 'vorvaerts durch technik?' Is this why they still drive on the wrong side of the road?

3. Who invented the guillotine?
    [1]   Victor Karam   [2]   Wilkinson Sword
    [3] Cut-throat Jake   [4]   Doctor Guillotin

4. 'From the storming of the Bastille to the rise of
    Napoleon, French politics was one big publicity
    stunt'. Discuss with reference to Paris Fashion
    Designers.

5. The French Revolution could not occur in this
    country because:-
    [1] Revolutions make too much noise [2] No one
    would notice [3] The Queen might object
    [4] This isn't France

6. Honi soit qui mal y pense?

A Glossary of Terms

ancien régime: old hat.

assemblée: see convention.

bourgeois: big bores.

calendar (revolutionary): invention to give people an excuse to forget other people's birthdays.

commission: see assemblée.

convention: see tribunal.

constitution: see assemblée, commission, convention, council and tribunal.

council: see commission.

coup d'état: open-top sports car.

Dauphin: Prince of Wales.

Dauphine: a car built by Renault with the engine in the back and everything else more or less where it should be.

département: shopping precinct (derived from liberté)

egalité: what's your's is mine and what's mine is mine.

fraternité: telling you what egalité means.

gâteaux: iron rations.

lettres de cachet: catch-phrases.

liberté: Paris department store.

marseillaise: salad cream.

noblesse oblige: to a manor born.

petit-bourgeois: yuppies.

paysan: prerevolutionary tax system, formed by the initial letters of Pay As You Starve As Normal.

revolution: change from paysan to saye; [Starve As You Earn]

sans-culottes: designer jeans

thermidor: month in revolutionary calendar named after a lobster.

tribunal: see council.

voltaire: primitive rechargable battery.

EDITORIAL NOTE

We have kept to the end, the headlines by which the Press carried, to an eagerly waiting world, the most famous words spoken during this period[1] – a time of countless memorable words and speeches. So many and so memorable that they have almost all been completely forgotten.

Some would say that these were the words that finally fanned into revolutionary flame the sparks of discontent and indignation among the people of France. But it has to be admitted that others could never see what all the fuss was about.

(see over)

---

1.   For the actual words readers are referred to p. 71, paragraph 3.

L'express

NOBLESSE OBLIGE

LE TEM...

ROYAL INTERVENTION
FOOD CRISIS

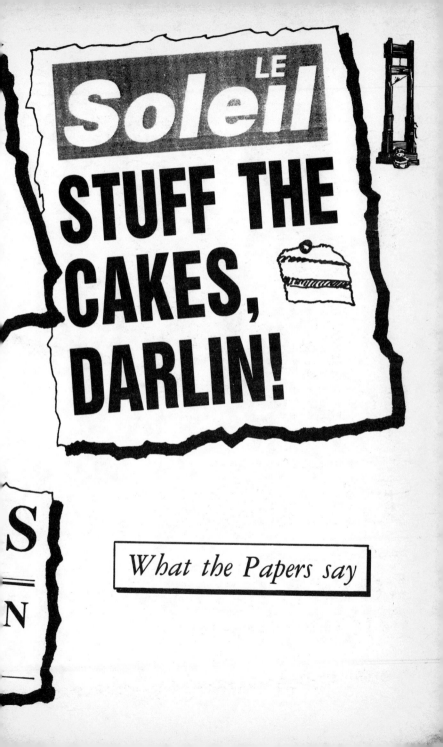

LE Soleil

STUFF THE CAKES, DARLIN!

What the Papers say

LA FIN?